ARCTIC AND ANTARCTIC

ARCTIC and ANTARCTIC

A Prospect of the Polar Regions

BY

COLIN BERTRAM

Director of the Scott Polar Research Institute, Cambridge, 1949–1956
Fellow and Tutor of St. John's College, Cambridge

CAMBRIDGE
W. HEFFER & SONS LTD.

| First Published | - | - | - | - | 1939 |
| New Edition (entirely revised) | | - | - | 1958 |

Printed in Great Britain at the Works of
W. HEFFER & SONS LTD., CAMBRIDGE, ENGLAND

DEDICATION:

THIS BOOK IS DEDICATED TO THE STAFF
OF THE SCOTT POLAR RESEARCH INSTITUTE
IN CAMBRIDGE, THAN WHOM NONE HAVE
DONE MORE TO FURTHER KNOWLEDGE
AND PERSPECTIVE OF POLAR AFFAIRS.

CHAPTER I

Introduction

IN considerable degree this book is a second edition of what I wrote in 1939 under the title *Arctic and Antarctic: the technique of polar travel*. Seventeen years have passed, eighteen years of change in the technique of polar travel and investigation, in political perspective and atmosphere, and indeed in the motivation of exploration and research. The writer on polar travel and affairs in the years before World War II was describing a little child, a child now embarked upon manhood, already growing tough.

With a perspective then widely acceptable I wrote as follows in 1939 in the Preface of *Arctic and Antarctic*.

"This book originated, and was partly written, during days of lying-up in the course of sledge journeys down in Graham Land in Antarctica. When the wind was tugging at the tent and the drift was rattling on the canvas, when travel was impossible, it was natural to wonder how and why one was yet moderately comfortable, and how it was that, though adequately fed, the stomach felt somewhat empty, and why the little bags by the stove contained precisely those foodstuffs that were inside them. Outside a dog might shake himself and whine with boredom, then once more curl up tightly against the blizzard, and the mind would begin to ponder the reasons why dogs are more efficient in sledge-hauling than men. Then, remembering the vivid accounts left by explorers of previous generations, their pains and troubles, their doubts and difficulties, there came the consideration of the foundations on which the new methods had been evolved; and to imagine in what ways present difficulties might in future be overcome. It was evident that the way of life in a polar land is based on tradition and experience, on inspired imagination and on trial and error. It was clear that there are principles, which though not realised in earlier days, have gradually emerged with the passage of time

1

and the growth of specialised research. Some of these principles seemed not to be understood as fully as might be supposed, even by those directly governed by them. The idea then came to me that it might be worth while attempting, not to record the narrative of an expedition, but to state some principles, physical, physiological and psychological, which govern the life of men in polar lands, presenting them in a way which might be of interest to others than specialists. When the attempt was made to follow out this plan, it soon became obvious that the underlying principles of dietary, housing and transport, could be far more attractively presented in a setting that depicted the life itself. An effort has been made to do this, in the hope of giving to others some true appreciation of the effect produced on the individual by the polar environment, by its peace and beauty, no less than by its cold and barrenness."

The intention now remains the same—to provide, not a text book, but a fair picture in true perspective of polar developments today, and to do this so far as possible in a manner that portrays life and experience. Much has changed but much remains the same. Geography, fauna, and the impact of personal isolation, remain; while mechanisation, political jockeying, and vastly increased scales of activity, are relative newcomers in the fields of polar endeavour.

As a matter of fact, and for purposes of useful comparison and contrast, the history of polar endeavour can be viewed in three well-marked stages. The 'pioneer' stage is the period before the first World War. The 'transitional' stage lies between the World Wars. And the 'modern' stage is that which has succeeded World War II. As between stages there are forerunners of the future and left-overs from the past, but in general these stages are well-defined and useful in the production of an understanding which is yet far less widespread than it has need to be.

The progress from stage to stage is largely to be measured in increasing complexity, and enlarged material resources. The simple motive of personal high endeavour, at any rate in Antarctica, has been transformed into national political aspiration. Descriptive science has changed into the most detailed physical investigations which will achieve new heights in the activities of the International Geophysical Year of 1957-58. Transport has changed from dog and man-drawn sledges to multi-engined aircraft landing without fear on icecap or on floating ice.

This present volume owes much to *Arctic and Antarctic* of seventeen years ago, written, as is now to be seen, near the end of the 'transitional' stage in polar history. Much is here quoted from that predecessor, in illustration of the 'pioneer' and 'transitional' stages. Some quotations, deliberately reproduced, will now seem naïve to those who know. But that very quality itself is an indication of the gulf between the 'transitional' stage and 'modern' times.

Yet it is well to remember that the 'transitional' stage lasted little over two decades. Men nursed in the 'pioneer' stage, the proper heroes of the great adventures of Edwardian and early following days, live on as elder statesmen in the polar councils of today. Happily so, but few are they, nurtured in 'pioneer' days, or even in the early 'transitional' phase, who now fully recognise, appreciate and understand the events, needs and significance of the present 'modern' era. Britons, with our great traditions and experience, most especially must learn, both in fact and in perspective, if we are to play our worthy part today.

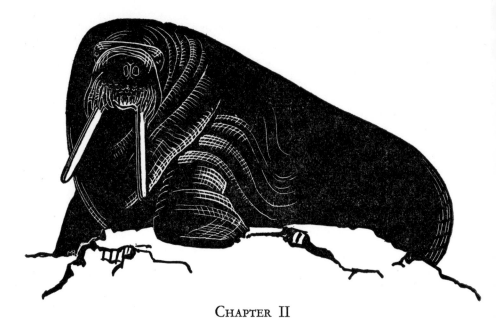

CHAPTER II

The Polar Regions and their Animals

"As knowledge increases, wonder deepens."—(Charles Morgan.)

A SHORT and precise definition of the 'polar regions' cannot be given because the term is vague, their extent varying according to the point of view from which they are considered. The geographer has decided to call 'polar' those regions that lie nearer than 23° 26′ 57″ of latitude to either Pole. The lines limiting these areas, the Arctic and Antarctic circles, are the lowest latitude at which the sun continues above the horizon for the whole twenty-four hours on midsummer's day. The botanist, on the other hand, lays stress upon those sinuous lines surrounding the extremities of the earth, and known as the 'limit of trees.' This line in the northern hemisphere varies in latitude by almost 20°, from about 52° N. in Labrador to 70° N. in northern Norway. Another bases his definition on arbitrary lines that represent the solution of formulae devised to take into account the average temperatures of the different months of the year. While the oceanographer will speak of the 'Antarctic

4

Convergence' which hydrographically and faunistically is a convenient limit.

We need not wonder that there are these different views of the extent of the polar regions when it is realised, for example, that the ice-bound coast of Labrador is in the latitude of England, that the southern extremity of Greenland is no further north than the Shetland Islands, that Pekin, with its biting winds and citizens with padded coats, is as far south as Greece, and that ice-encumbered South Georgia is in about the same south latitude as Brighton is in the north.

But there is one particular attribute of the polar regions however they are defined, namely, cold. Extreme cold of course exists, apart from polar lands, at the tops of high mountains, and in the centres of the great land masses of North America and Eurasia in winter. But except for the very highest mountains, this cold is a seasonal phenomenon, alternating with periods of very considerable warmth. To use another's words: "In the forests of north-east Siberia the temperature sinks lower every winter than it does anywhere on the Arctic coast, and a prairie city like Winnipeg, one of the world's greatest wheat centres, regularly has degrees of cold that can compare with those in the Arctic. It is the length of winter, coupled with the feeble summer heat, that dominates the climate." The cold governs the appearance of the land and sea surfaces, and the lives of the animals and plants that are found there. Where not completely covered by ice, the land is often bare and rocky, soil is scarce and vegetation scant, lakes and boggy ground are common in summer, and snow and ice masses are abundant on the higher ground. For many feet the sub-soil is permanently frozen, only the uppermost layers melting in summer, so that drainage is poor and the surface waterlogged. The floating ice of sea and lakes breaks and diminishes in summer, but much of it often remains to the following winter.

On the other hand the locking up of water as ice may produce a desert, as physiologically real as any of the arid regions of the earth, where are found drought-resisting forms of plant life, and a general poverty of fauna and flora. In fact, one of the great dangers to polar plants is this risk of desiccation, by a continued loss of water to the air at times when there is no protective covering of snow, and when water cannot be absorbed by the roots because it is in the form of ice.

Of more immediate interest are the effects of cold, not upon plants, but upon animals. The rate of a chemical reaction is directly determined by the temperature, and since life itself is dependent upon chemical reactions, it is apparent that animal activity is largely controlled by the temperature of the individual's surroundings. When an insect is subjected to a low temperature the chemical reactions in its body may be so retarded that it cannot even move its legs. In England, the sluggishness of butterflies on the colder days of summer is well-known. For some Arctic insects it has been shown that there may be no more than half a dozen days in the whole year warm enough for them to walk about, mate, and lay their eggs. But on these few warm days they appear in myriads dancing in the sunlight, retiring to the shelter of the rocks and vegetation when the temperature falls. There are considerable variations in the lowest temperatures at which these small creatures may be active. Some of the Arctic spiders and flies can still carry on an active life at several degrees below freezing point. On account of the chilling effect upon the animal's activity, reptiles and other cold-blooded forms, are not found in higher latitudes. Warm-blooded animals, on the other hand, have adopted a means by which their vital chemical reactions are unaffected by outside cold and the changing temperatures of their surroundings. Their internal 'environment,' being constant, allows of a far more delicate balance and control of the innumerable processes inside the living organism. But the maintenance of a standard body temperature many degrees above that of the air in a cold region is clearly difficult. The larger the animal the less difficult will it be, because of the greater ratio of mass and volume to the surface area of the body. The Polar Bear has a great body mass all at a temperature of about 98° F., but relatively a very small surface area through which the heat is lost. On the other hand, a lemming has a tiny body, but proportionately a much greater surface through which its heat is dissipated.

While cold is the chief feature of both polar regions, there is one enormous difference between the two areas. The northern is mainly water, the southern mostly land. This great divergence as to the distribution of land and water in the two polar regions is the basal cause behind a whole multitude of other differences. The north polar area is an ocean that is covered by pack-ice even a dozen feet thick, often the accumulation of several winters. This pack, broken and contorted, gradually filters out of the polar basin, mainly as a heavy stream which continually flows southwards down the eastern coast of Greenland. Surrounding this ocean are land masses which, except for Greenland and Nordaustlandet, are free of perpetual ice at sea-level. In these land masses there is a gradual transition from the Arctic climate in the north, down to the temperate regions further south. The southern polar region is in very striking contrast. It is a huge isolated continent, for the most part a plateau at over 6,000 feet, completely covered by an icecap of enormous thickness that descends everywhere to sea-level. Surrounding this land of Antarctica is the Southern Ocean containing a few widely scattered islands of sub-polar type. Into this ocean drift vast quantities of ice, calved from the continental mass, or formed by the freezing of inshore waters. So it comes about that a visitor to the North Pole drifts upon a moving floe, while his brother in Antarctica must climb to a height of over 9,000 feet if he would stand at the southern extremity of the earth.

Remembering this first great difference it is possible to understand the other differences consequent upon it. Being high and completely ice-covered, the south polar area has a far lower average temperature than the north, this being more marked in summer than in winter. The southern continent proper has, in fact, not one month of the year in which the average temperature rises even to freezing point. On account of its isolation and its coldness* the Antarctic has not now, nor

* The minimal temperatures so far recorded on the earth's surface are near −68° C. (or −90° F.) in Siberia, and a few degrees less severe in the Yukon and on the Greenland icecap. The lowest recorded in Antarctica is about −60·5° C. (or −77° F.). "The real severity of the Antarctic climate is not shown in its low minimum temperatures, but in its low maximum temperatures."—(*Polar Record*, Vol. 6, No. 46, July 1953, p. 822.)

ever has had, any indigenous human occupation, and in fact possesses no land animals at all, other than a few tiny mites and insects. The birds essentially are marine animals. But the Artic regions, having warm summers and being continuous with more temperate lands, support a fauna that includes, besides innumerable tiny forms, such large animals as man, the Musk Ox and the Polar Bear. Its flora too is greatly richer, including more than four hundred species of the higher plants, while the Antarctic can boast but two (a grass and a tiny 'pink'), and these live only on its very verge.

Despite the northern lands being less harsh than those of the south, clearly, if animals and plants are to live there, they must possess peculiar vigour and special adaptations with which to contend the severity of their surroundings. The 'providential fitness of the environment' for the existence of life should be recognised no less than the fitness of the organisms for that environment. A single example of this environmental fitness, that alone makes such a complex as life possible, may be found in the peculiar qualities of ice and water. Water has a greater capacity for heat than almost any other substance; it is inert and a fine solvent. Unlike the generality of substances water expands on freezing, and ice therefore floats. Were it not so the oceans of the world would be solid ice, with lakes of slush upon their surface, for the summer sun would be unable to melt the accumulation from the cold of the previous polar winter.

Climatic fluctuations must be recognised, of a short term and of a long term nature, and indeed of a very long term nature. The difficulty is to decide within which order of magnitude present demonstrable fluctuations fall. Alterations in the north are more clear as yet than those of the south. Undoubtedly in the so-called 'Middle Ages' of the historians, Greenland became climatically more harsh and the Norsemen vanished. More recently there has been an amelioration of northern climate and probably now the state is much as it was in the Norsemen's heyday. Sheep again are being reared in south-west Greenland, and cod have largely replaced seals as the hunters' quarry.

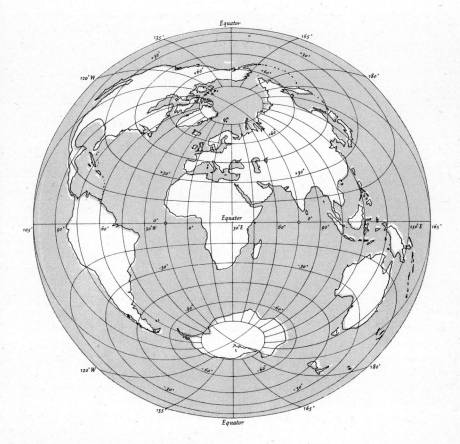

DOUBLY EQUIDISTANT
PROJECTION OF THE SPHERE
giving distances true from two
points ⊙ on the Equator 90° apart

Published by permission of the
Royal Geographical Society

The history of the recent development of the Russian Northern Sea Route seems to tell the same tale. Some assert that the area of floating ice in the arctic basin and its effluent streams has decreased by 20 per cent. since 1900. Now there is some indication that since 1940 this trend may have been reversed, but steadily improving navigational aids have largely masked the effect.

Being in direct contact with temperate lands the Arctic regions seem for millennia to have had their human inhabitants of varying cultures. The Eskimos, Aleuts and Chukchis of today remind us of the vigour, resourcefulness and cheerfulness of those who inhabit the harsh places of the earth. One wonders if it was true that the Eskimos, having no cereals, saps or other carbohydrates available, were the only people of the world who had never discovered the pleasurable advantages of alcohol. Certainly today all these primitive peoples are in cultural flux as perhaps most strangely typified by the Canadian Eskimo boy, aged seven, who happily turns from his mother's breast to the stranger's offered cigarette.

The inhabitants of northern lands account for no more than a tiny fraction of the world's total of people, and their numbers, after considerable falls following the introduction of the white man's infectious diseases, now rise but slowly. The world's total population in 1957 is near 2,700 million,* and it is an odd reflection that more than three-quarters of these live out their lives in less than a quarter of the world's habitable area.

Despite this crowding, the dwellers in highly cultivated and populous lands, the inhabitants of England as a whole, have no realisation of the natural abundance of life. They see the trees, they see the grass, the fields of golden corn and root crops with their shiny leaves, but do not think of these as life. These grow but do not move until the wind shakes them in its passing. It is movement that to most men is the epitome of life, the galloping of horses, the flight of birds, the wriggling of lambs' tails as they take their morning suck. But the movements of men themselves and their astonishing abundance are forgotten by reason of

* Seventeen years ago when the first edition of this book was published the figure for world population was close to 2,000 million.

their familiarity and it is only the athlete's prowess that remains a pleasure to his fellows. A crowd of adult males, in sombre bowler hats, rotund dark figures with spread umbrellas trotting gently down an incline to the railway station, excites no thrill of wonder. Yet, if a spirit of change came among them, if, like the earth-bound chrysalis that sheds its wrappings and emerges a perfect butterfly, these sombre humans were metamorphosed into a herd of reindeer with tall branching antlers and glossy flanks, trotting down the hillside to cross a mountain brook, men's hearts would leap with startled pleasure, and they would follow every movement of the herd with admiration. But in modern Britain such sights are lacking. There are left none of the larger animals untamed, nothing but deer in the Highlands and seals in the Wash, and rarely enough to give a thrilling wonder at the sight of great abundance. In Saxon times there were still reindeer in the north of Scotland, and bears in the forests. The Normans saw wolves and boars and deer in plenty, and beavers built their castles in the rivers. Now all are gone, and the massed marvels inland are confined to wheeling flocks of starlings as they travel to their roosts, and on the coasts to herrings, and sea birds on the cliffs. So in the England of today most people miss the joyous wonder that belongs to man when he comes in contact with vast numbers of animals, and the larger those animals the greater is the wonder. For those who have never experienced it, this feeling of wonder is difficult to understand. It is the adult manifestation, so many times enlarged, of the emotions of the small boy as he holds in his hands, all scaly and glistening, the first large fish that he has caught unaided.

Though it seems that this sensation, this feeling of natural wonder, is almost lost in England, it is one of the great attractions of polar lands, and the seas that surround them, for on many of those shores the original abundance of life still exists. In those colder climes the effect is magnified, for besides the contrast with adjacent barrenness, it seems to be the rule that where species are few the numbers shall be great. As a simple example, take one from the insect world. On the down-wind shore of Arctic lakes is sometimes found in great quantities a peculiar grey-brown sludge that could be shovelled into barrels. This sludge is a collection of the floating skins of countless hordes of tiny gnats, shed as they emerged from the water for their brief aerial existence.

But in polar lands there are fewer beasts than once there were. Besides others, the Greenland Right Whale and the Southern Fur Seal have been virtually exterminated, though happily there is now some indication of a gradual rebuilding of populations in a few remote areas. Others are now rare where once they were multitudinous, because man in his search for wealth has slaughtered them. Almost all the sub-Antarctic islands had once their monster herds of Elephant Seals, and the walrus of the north lay in contented thousands on the beaches. Today, the Atlantic Walrus in large numbers is only to be found around Zemlya Frantsa-Iosifa and north of Baffin Bay. Still, there the monster will hook his enquiring tusks over the gunwales of small boats as he did to Nansen. Then the remedy, so it is said, is boldly to seize the tusks with the bare hands and gently to return the creature to its proper element without exciting its anger. Björnöya, soon after it was discovered, was the scene of the most extensive walrus slaughtering. Once, in 1604, Stephen Bennett and his companions killed between seven and eight hundred in six hours. "When all our shot and powder was spent, we would blow their eyes out with a little pease shot, and then come on the blind side of them and with a carpenter's axe cleave their heads." From another voyage to the same island, Bennett returned with "31 tunnes of Oyle, and one hogshead, one barrell, and one terce of Morses teeth: beside 400 other teeth." For the most part the great herds of walrus were slaughtered for their tusks alone, the carcases lying to rot in the mossy valleys. Today, the walrus is extinct in southern Svalbard, and only the broken, whitening skulls, overgrown with grass and saxifrage, remain in tragic witness to the past.

At last, though very gradually, more people are realising that it is better policy to protect the goose and to be contented with its golden eggs. In the present century, for example, the Elephant Seal of South Georgia has been protected by the

British Colonial Administration. The killing is controlled, and a suitable proportion of the adult bulls alone is taken, so allowing a rational harvest to be gained each year without depletion of the stock of this polygamous species. Too slowly such control is being extended to other animals and in other places. One wonders whether the descendants of our grandchildren will be able to thank them in a way that we cannot thank our ancestors, and in a way that we ourselves may never be thanked. But perhaps this is too gloomy. The present International Whaling Convention is a remarkable instrument which, if it continues to be applied effectively and even more stringently, may be a monument to the idealistic zoologists of the mid-twentieth century. Likewise great praise is due to the United States authorities for their splendid rational conservation and harvesting of the Alaskan Fur Seal of the Pribilof Islands in Bering Sea.

Despite such ruthless slaughter great numbers of the larger animals do still survive in polar lands, and still in places can one come to feel the great wonder of the multitude of life. But the polar regions are lands of extreme contrast: in one place there is a teeming plenteousness, seals, penguins or caribou, while a few miles distant the land will be empty, no living thing breaking in upon its silent stillness. It is the local concentrations of animals that are the wonder, for these cold lands, treated as a whole, possess but very little life. Indeed, except at the sea's edge, the whole great southern continent maintains no living thing save only a few small mosses and lichens, and some tiny mites that live among them. Apart from the two large herbivores, the Caribou or Reindeer and the Musk Ox that wander in the lands that border the north polar ocean, all the larger polar animals are dependent on the sea, either living in it or obtaining their food from it. So the hungry traveller in a polar land must hug the coast, for that is where he finds his food.

The mainstay of all coastal polar life is that group of mammals known as seals, of which there are many, though different species, both Arctic and Antarctic. For long there have been great commercial seal fisheries for skins and blubber, but these do not concern the individual polar traveller except that now

there is less food for him than once there was. Most species
of seals are gregarious, at least in the breeding season, and this
applies both to the agile, sub-polar Eared seals (the Fur seals and
Sea lions) and the True seals, more sluggish on land since they
are more perfectly adapted for the water. It is a splendid thing
to see a rookery of seals, whether on the winter ice or upon
some spreading beach. The stout matron seals in groups and
coteries lie upon their sides, each one's new-born pup beside
her, staring with round pathetic eyes at the surrounding polar
ice. Or it may be a great gathering on some open beach of a
species where the bulls, not content with a single female, keep
a harem as large as their fighting skill can manage. It is so with
the Elephant Seals of the sub-Antarctic islands, which in some
places breed in countless thousands. The cows, their season
come, leave the sea to pup, and the monster bulls, some even
20 ft. in length, herd them into groups and keep them there.
The pups are born, and in a few days' time the adults mate again
and that is when the fighting comes. From dawn till dark the
enormous bulls bluster and roar, distending their leathery noses
in their fury, rearing up their bulk on high to crash down on
their adversaries, to gash them with their teeth. One enemy
beaten by fight or by bluff the harem bull must surely wish for
rest, but this he can never have. A younger male has poached
a cow on the far side of his harem, and the breeding bull must
rush his ponderous bulk to the attack. He takes no heed of
cows and pups, but charges over them, bellowing at his rival
until, once more a conqueror, he turns but to fight again. This
great bull, and his harem containing even thirty cows, is but one
tiny fraction of the whole enormous gathering on the beach,
and this beach is a single one of the dozens that surround the
island. Most wonderful of all, these prodigious bulls, these
great masses of raging bone and muscle, remain active upon the
beaches a full six weeks on end, and not once do they leave
their cows, not once do they return into the sea, not once in all
those weeks do they take a particle of food.

   That is South Georgia, and likewise in essentials is the great
herd of breeding Fur seals at the Pribilof Islands in Bering Sea.
There, it is said, may be seen at one moment more large mammals

than is visible together at any other point on earth, and to have seen is certainly to believe.

Just as the species of seal in the north and south are different, so is their behaviour. In the north the skill of the hunter must be great, whether he watches silently at the breathing-hole, or stalks with rifle and kayak, and often he will fail to kill. In the south it is very different. Seamen, clumsy in big boots, laughing and shouting, can walk straight to the unwitting sleepy seals to shoot them, stun them, or gash their throats. The tame folly of the Antarctic seals is pitiable, ignorant of terrestrial perils, and with no enemy outside the water but man. In the south, after a few days of seeming paradise, the Eskimo would pine from boredom, so simple is the hunting and so placid the quarry. It is a strange experience to stand upon a small and isolated floe, as it rocks gently in the swell, with its surface covered by the bodies of a score of silvery seals. Then some are shot and butchered, but their brothers lie placidly as before, hardly stirring but to grunt and raise their eyes when touched, unmoving as another's blood trickles beneath their silken bellies. On the floes these southern seals lie in perfect peace, ignoring even man the slaughterer. In the water they are swift and alert, ever watchful to escape their enemy the Killer Whale. Despite their wariness and speed, almost every seal bears upon its body at least one set of scars, the everlasting marks of gashes inflicted by rows of pointed teeth that have barely been escaped. Those are the so-called Crabeater Seals of the Antarctic pack ice, living almost entirely upon the crustacean Euphausids which too are the staple diet of the great whales of the Southern Ocean. These Crabeater Seals, whose breeding congregations on the pack ice have never yet been seen, are probably the most abundant of all the seals.

Seals in the north are the means of life for the Eskimo, and are the main natural source of food for the foreign traveller in polar lands. Upon seals the simple traveller can feed himself and feed his dogs when they journey together along the polar shores or across the Arctic sea. Likewise, whales swim near all polar coasts, though to the individual traveller they are a spectacle rather than a source of food. But bold Eskimos, even with their primitive equipment, do kill the smaller kinds for food, and prize the Narwhal's tusk.   And just as the sea provides food for the fish, the whales and the seals, so it does for the birds which nest in colonies round polar shores.

All kinds of bird are good for food, sustaining life, but some are pleasant in the eating, and some are less so.   Fortunately for the hungry human many of these colonial polar birds are so tame that they may be caught with the hands, and, for the most part, their eggs are large.   Some of these birds breed together in prodigious numbers; geese, ducks, auks and gulls in the north; penguins, petrels and gulls in the south.   There are places where birds sit nesting, close-packed side by side, the whole great concourse covering many acres.   The noise is tremendous, as of a huge human crowd shouting in the distance, swelling and sinking, rising and falling, the shrill pipings of the young mingling with the deeper cries of the adults.   So it goes on through the everlasting daylight of the polar summer, birds coming and going, flying and walking, living and dying and hatching.   Inland too in Arctic countries there are sometimes many birds, geese, ducks and divers, though all are usually more shy than their fellows on the coast.   But Eider Ducks, sitting upon their down-lined nests may, with patience, be snared by hand.   The Eider is a lover of lake islets of the north.   As the female, brown and mottled, compact, watchful and unmoving, broods her large green eggs, it takes a practised eye quickly to distinguish her from the hummocked vegetation round about, until her bright, black eye and horny bill betray her.

The species of truly polar mammals that go inland, and are not dependent on the sea, are very few.   Chief of these are the two large herbivores, the circumpolar Reindeer, and the Musk Ox, which is more limited in its range.   The Reindeer in Arctic Eurasia has long been semi-domesticated, tribes being wholly dependent on it for food, transport and clothing.   In the Canadian Arctic archipelago there is the Caribou, a variety of the Reindeer, but it is not found in the most northerly of the islands, nor has it been domesticated.   Across Smith Sound the animals migrate, and thence they have spread to populate the west Greenland coast.   Likewise, via the northern route they populated the east coast, almost meeting others that, rounding Kapp Farvel, spread northwards from the south. Reindeer were seen in east Greenland as recently as 1880, but since then, from an unknown cause, they have become extinct. But still on the east Greenland coast their cast antlers are a common feature on the pastures at the heads of the fjords.

More limited in its distribution is that other essentially Arctic herbivore, the Musk Ox, the exciting beast of youthful tales, with hair so long upon its belly that by repute it rubs out its own footprints in the snow so that none can see where it has passed. It is found in the northern Canadian islands, and in north and east Greenland, but it has never penetrated south of Scoresby Sound. The Musk Ox lives a roaming life, seeking the scattered tufts of coarse, dry grass on which it feeds. The odd tail-less beast makes fine eating, but there are now widespread protective measures designed to save it from the extermination that it has suffered in many of its former haunts. Though apparently so ponderous, in reality the Musk Ox is an animal of considerable agility, and over boulder-strewn moraines, or high arctic pastures, can run much faster than a man.

Three further strictly Arctic mammals can hardly be considered as satisfactory sources of food for men. These are the Polar Wolf, fox and lemming, though certainly all of them are edible. The wolf is rare and hard to catch, fox flesh is scarcely pleasant, while it would take many lemmings to make even the smallest pie. More useful is the Arctic Hare, a beautiful creature, pure white except for the black tips to the ears. It is shy but often plentiful, and it has saved men from starvation in northern Greenland.

The Polar Bear is widespread along all Arctic coasts. It is not limited to regions of lowly vegetation, but is free to wander by land and sea in search of seals to kill and explorers to menace. It wanders great distances over the ice of the polar sea and inland from the coasts, and even has been met far inland on the Greenland icecap. The meat is good, but the liver has somewhat toxic qualities, resulting from its excessively high content of vitamin A. The adult bear is possessed of a greater ability to travel than almost any other animal. A very powerful, though slow, swimmer, it is undeterred by many miles of open sea. It can equally well cover, at surprising speed, great distances on land or over ice, and is possessed of an astonishing agility in clambering up the cliffs. It is a sight worth going very far to see to watch a large she-bear, followed by her twin cubs a half-year old, mounting step by step a steep and rocky headland. The mother leads, her young ones close behind. She stands erect and sniffs and paws the rock above, then finds an easier way and traverses a narrow ledge, where her very width one would suppose must be her downfall. But she crosses with apparent ease, then nimbly mounts the scree beyond, while the cubs, unhesitating, follow step by step.

Such are the animals on which man may feed in polar lands. The plants are much less useful to him, though certain tribes of Eskimo make greater use of vegetation than has often been supposed. The Antarctic, so completely bare of inland animals, is likewise without plants, except for a few sparse tufts of moss and small encrusting lichens. The northern flora contains many species, and a variety of forms have been eaten under the stress of imminent starvation. Polar vegetation does provide two useful species, long-known for their anti-scorbutic properties, the Arctic Scurvy Grass and the sub-Antarctic Kerguelen Cabbage, both of them cruciferous plants.

The value of vegetable supplies to seamen of earlier days is well shown in the words of James Weddell, that most enterprising of Enderby Brothers' captains, writing in 1825 in his *Voyage Towards the South Pole.*

"Our arrival here (South Georgia), though it was not a country the most indulgent, we considered to be a very happy event. Our sailors had suffered much from cold fogs and wet during the two months they had been navigating the south; and as we had been nearly five months under sail, the appearance of scurvy (that disease so fatally attendant upon long voyages) was to be dreaded. Our vessels too were so much weather beaten, that they greatly needed refitting; so that taking into account our many pressing wants, this island, though inhospitable, was capable of affording us great relief. Our crews here fed plenteously on greens which, although bitter, are very salutary, being an excellent antiscorbutic: with regard to meat, we were supplied with young albatrosses, that is to say, about a year old: the flesh of these is sweet, but not sufficiently firm to be compared with that of any domestic fowl."

Though in polar lands such sources of food are great in certain places, in general, this life is concentrated along the coasts, and is for the most part seasonal. Huge areas of the north and the whole hinterland of the southern continent have no local offering to the hopeful traveller.

CHAPTER III

Polar Living

Serve God daily, love one another, preserve your victuals, beware of
fire, and keepe good companie."
—Sir John Hawkins's Orders to his Fleet (1564).)

THIS chapter deals a little with physiology and acclimatisation
in our own species, and then discourses briefly on clothing both
past and present, and in theory and in practice. There follow
certain descriptions of living on long polar journeys, comparing
the hardships of the 'pioneer' stage with the adequacy and quiet
contentment of the 'transitional' phase. The 'transitional' way
of life has in fact of course now largely been superseded by the
advance of the mechanised 'modern' phase wherein the tractor

19

pulls a wannegan, so, like the snail, carrying into the wilderness
a comfortable house.   None the less, detailed descriptions of
'transitional' tent life still have their interest and value.

Man, like all the other mammals and the birds, is homoio-
thermous.   That is to say his whole physiological and mental
construction and efficiency depend upon the maintenance of a
standard high internal temperature.   Any important departure
from normality leads quickly to inadequacy and death.   The
maintenance of the high uniform body temperature is the
guiding principle in the life of the human organism in a cold
country.   This standard temperature is controlled by an extremely delicate mechanism, balancing the relative rates of heat
production and heat loss.   When the body temperature tends
to fall too low, more combustion may be induced by voluntary
muscular exercise or by involuntary shivering: when the body
needs to be cooled, sweating occurs, and heat is rapidly lost by
evaporation.

That is the stabilising mechanism, but the individual normally is hardly conscious of it.   When the nerve endings in his
skin tell him of the cold, man first of all eats warming food and
covers his hairless body with more layers of clothing, often
made from the skins of other animals.   Or he can get closer to
a fire, or spend more on space-heating.   But if these attempts
are not enough he will soon begin to suffer.   First he feels the
cold in his extremities, his toes, his nose, his ears.   Then the
body, in its efforts to protect itself, contracts the little blood-
vessels near the skin, so that the hot blood flows more deeply
down, away from the surface, where its heat is being wasted.
The warm and ruddy appearance of the skin is lost, and though
this is of general advantage to the body, the reaction leaves a
local danger.   For now the surface itself may freeze, and hard
white patches, frostbites, soon appear.   These first frostbites do
no harm if treated at once by gentle outside warmth, but should
the freezing go more deeply or last for long, the tissue cells are
killed.   Then the flesh will later rot, and leave an open wound.
Should the outside cold become even more intense, and the
individual be still unable to insulate himself by external means,
then as his body becomes stiff and numb so does his brain cease

to function with its normal clarity. A little longer and the cold wins, for the man will die.

Frostbite, and actual freezing of the tissues, is an important study in itself. Opinion as to its most satisfactory treatment has swung markedly from decade to decade. Medical opinion now recommends rapid warming in a bath not exceeding 45° C. Much experimental work has been done and is being continued.*

An experiment in deliberate personal cooling, by a professor of physiology, still has its interest:

"What comes back when I recall the attempt to reduce my body temperature? About the effects on the heart I have told you: they were interesting but in no way arresting, but what comes back is the effect on my mind. In each of the two experiments that I performed there was a moment when my whole mental outlook altered. As I lay naked in the cold room at Wood's Hole I had been shivering and my limbs had been flexed in a sort of effort to huddle up, and I had been very conscious of the cold. Then a moment came when I stretched out my legs; the sense of coldness passed away, it was succeeded by a beautiful feeling of warmth: the word 'bask' most fitly described my condition; I was basking in the cold. What had taken place, I suppose, was that my central nervous system . . . had given up the fight . . . and that the blood returning (to the skin) gave that sensation of warmth which one experiences when one goes out of a cold storage room into the ordinary air. I suppose too, that had the experiment not ended at that point my temperature would have fallen rapidly and that I was on the verge of the condition of travellers when they go to sleep in extreme cold, never again to wake. And I was conscious of other reversions of mental state; not only was there a physical extension of the limbs, but with it came a change in the general mental attitude. The natural apprehension lest some person alien to the experiment should enter the room and find me quite unclad disappeared—just as flexion was changed to extension, so the natural modesty was changed to—well I don't know what. Clearly one should be very cautious about taking these liberties with one's mind—and that is the point, the higher parts of the central nervous system were the first things to suffer."

—(Joseph Barcroft in *The Architecture of Physiological Function.*)

The insulating powers of channel swimmers and what to do when ship-wrecked in cold seas, are both relevant in the present context. It would seem that stout, well-insulated persons may, by struggling or swimming, maintain their body heat; but thin individuals suffer a more rapid drop in body temperature when they are swimming than when they keep still. 'Traditional

* See *Polar Record*, Vol. 7, No. 47, January 1954, p. 51.

naval advice to cling to wreckage in order to conserve strength would appear, therefore, to be sound.'*

Though man cannot do so himself, some warm-blooded animals can make a temporary armistice with the cold of their environment. The armistice is hibernation, and its price is inactivity. The hibernation may be partial or complete, either a quiescence in a place chosen so that heat losses from the body are at a minimum, or a change to another physiological state, another point of equilibrium, with the body temperature standardised at a lower level, a state resembling sleep in the passive inactivity of the organism. The pregnant female Polar Bear goes into a semi-hibernation, for weeks or months, until her twin cubs are born, but though she is quiescent and fasting, so far as is known, there is no lowering of her body temperature. The rodents are the real exponents of the art of hibernation. Some wake at long intervals to feed, but the dormouse, lemming and others hibernate for many months, fasting and unmoving, curled in a comfortable nest. In them the body temperature falls many degrees, perhaps even from 100° F. to 40° F., where it remains except for slight changes following the major variations of the outside air.

In hibernation all the bodily processes are retarded and respiration and the pulse are exceedingly slow. The awakening is remarkable. The necessary stimuli being applied naturally or artificially, the pulse and respiration quicken, and then starts a violent shivering, convulsive in its intensity. The body temperature begins to rise at once, and in an hour the transition is complete. The body temperature will by then be normal, and the animal with regained activity will be hungrily searching for food. Such is one method of ignoring the cold at its most bitter. Man cannot hibernate in the true sense, but a tendency towards partial hibernation was exhibited, so it was said, by some of the natives of northern Asia. With them it was the custom in the winter for the whole family to sleep hour upon hour, day upon day, huddled round the stove, only waking to eat morsels of food and to stoke the fire.

* See *Polar Record*, Vol. 6, No. 44, July 1952, p. 535 and Vol. 8, No. 53, May 1956, p. 176.

Sledge party returning through water during the month of July. From a drawing by
Cdr. W. W. May in his *Series of Fourteen Sketches made during the Voyage up Wellington
Channel*, 1852. Day. 1855.

Towing with dogs on the Yenisej. From a drawing by Professor R. D. Holm in *The
Voyage of the Vega*, by A. E. Nordenskiöld. MacMillan. 1881.

Lapp Akja. From an unsigned drawing in *The Voyage of the Vega,* by A. E. Nordenskiöld. MacMillan. 1881.

Sledges of the Eskimaux. From a drawing by Capt. Lyon in *Parry's Second Voyage,* 1821-23. John Murray. 1824.

Normally, however, polar man does successfully fight the low temperature of his surroundings by insulating his body with its high standard temperature by means of clothes and houses. As an example of the greatest insulation, consider a rich citizen in the cold of the North American winter. He lives in a centrally-heated set of apartments, with air conditioned as to temperature and humidity: his bed is warm and comfortable, his food and drink are placed within reach. When he finds it necessary to encounter the chill of the outside winter air, he does so at ease in a fur coat and a closed and heated car. He may well be contrasted with certain of his fellows on this earth who, having neither the means nor the skill so to insulate themselves from the cold, only just managed to survive the rigours of their surroundings.

To quote the diary of Charles Darwin, writing in 1834 of the inhabitants of Tierra del Fuego: "Here five of six human beings, naked and uncovered from the wind, rain and snow in this tempestuous climate, sleep on the wet ground, curled up like animals. In the morning they rise to pick shell-fish at low water; and the women, winter and summer, dive to collect sea-eggs; such miserable food is eked out by berries and fungi." "I would willingly," wrote James Weddel in 1825, "for the honour of human nature, raise these neglected people somewhat higher in the scale of intellectual estimation than they have reached; but I must acknowledge their condition to be that of the lowest of mankind. At this age of the world, it appears almost incredible, and certainly disgraceful, that there should still exist such a tractable people in almost pristine ignorance." These poor natives, with a guanaco skin flung across their shoulders, shiver at the foot of the evolutionary ladder of insulation from the cold, while the rich citizen smiles down on them from the summit.

The mention of space-heating leads naturally to considerations of acclimatisation; does it really exist; what is it; and is it significant? Subjectively, acclimatisation to cold conditions undoubtedly exists and may be important. But objectively, its proof and measurement has been more difficult. However in recent years satisfactory tests of one aspect of it have been

c

devised, mostly in the form of measurable digital sensation and dexterity. But much remains to done in the assessment of total physiological acclimatisation.

However acclimatisation may be of no more than marginal significance, of importance perhaps to humble travellers, trappers and Eskimos, but scarcely to the modern masters of material resources who carry their environment with them to high latitudes. The body will never acclimatise to a degree that can be helpful in the cold by day, if nights are spent in the highly-heated atmospheres now considered normal by North American standards. That acclimatisation exists is very clear. The Briton, newly entered into the trans-Atlantic heated home, and the North American in a British household in winter, both suffer with more or less politeness and fortitude the discomforts of a changed environment. Each is forced to realize the extent of his personal adaptation to his accustomed home.

Our normal personal insulation, clothes, need next consideration, and their specialisation for high polar use are the result of long years of trial and ingenuity.

Clothing may be divided into several categories according to its purpose. There is clothing for physical protection, like armour, mackintoshes, sunhats and flynets. There is clothing for ornamentation, delight and modesty, be it bikini or brocaded gown. There are clothes and devices to alter the shape more nearly to that which is held to be desirable: corsets and the copper wire round the necks of certain Africans are examples. And then there are clothes whose purpose is insulation, whether like topee to keep out the sun's heat, or like fur trousers to retain the body's warmth. It is with this last category that polar travellers are most concerned, though not exclusively. With the ornamentation of his person the Eskimo may sometimes be concerned, but the normal polar traveller is not, though brightly-coloured garments have a cheering psychological effect, and have even been a requirement for those receiving financial aid from magazines desiring coloured illustrations.

The suitable covering of the hands and feet, particularly the latter, has always been of difficulty for they are very vulnerable. However lovely the feet of infants, the ordinary white man's naked foot has all too commonly become a thing disgusting, soft and misshapen, worse in the female than in the male. Compare these flabby appendages with the horny feet of men unused to shoes. The sole is half an inch thick of sound hard skin, and unlike shoe leather, it has the advantage that it thickens instead of being worn away in use. But in spite of this horny skin, really sharp thorns and stones may penetrate to the quick. The wound produced is variously treated. An Arab sailor who had punctured the sole of his foot on a sharp spike of coral was seen to light a small fire, and apply a glowing stick to the hole, so sealing it. He smelt the singeing skin with pleasure, smiled, and said it did not hurt. Despite such easy repair there has been a general attempt among primitive peoples to gain some form of foot protection. A tribe of Patagonian Indians cunningly solved the problem by skinning the lower part of a horse's leg in such a way that it remained tubular. This, when raw and soft, was pulled on over the foot and ankle. The open end was roughly tied, and the owner had but to sit by the fire until his feet were dry. He then had a durable, perfectly fitting pair of boots that need not, and in fact could not, be removed until cut off when worn with over-use. Such boots may be compared with those resistant foot protectors sometimes worn by Central European geese and turkeys. There it was the custom to drive large flocks of birds great distances along the stony roads to market. With such treatment there was a danger of unprotected feet being so damaged that the birds would walk with difficulty and lose value. The problem was ingeniously solved by first marching the birds through alternate pans of liquid tar and sand, so sending them off to market each with a pair of fine strong boots.

Despite explanatory research, wonder is not assuaged when one contemplates the easy complacency with which polar birds, without benefit of boots, stand for hours upon ice at many degrees below zero.

In clothing people in polar regions the retention of warmth is the primary aim, with certain modifications and additions, as protection for the feet and from the wet. Also the eyes must be guarded against the excessive, blinding light. The principle of all clothing that has warmth as its chief function is to cover the surface of the body with a layer of material that is a bad conductor of heat. That is to say, an effort is made to reduce to a minimum the continual passage of the body's internal heat to the cold atmosphere without. The simplest and most convenient non-conductor of heat is air. Unless we are to consider the asbestos suits of fire-fighters, where the insulation is to prevent the passage of heat in the opposite direction, it is true to say that all* warm clothes depend on air. All the hairy and feathered creatures of the earth are able by their natural coats to retain a stable non-conducting layer of air against their skins. Since humans are by nature more naked than their brother beasts, man has been obliged to clothe himself in a protective layer of stable air by his own ingenious efforts. In primitive tribes this is done by covering the body with the pelts of other animals. In their simplest use a skin is merely flung across the shoulders, and loosely tied around the neck. Weddell, in 1825, writing of the dwellers in Tierra del Fuego, remarks: "The only clothing the males wear is a skin over their shoulders, reaching little more than half-way down the back; some have not even this sorry garment. The women have generally a larger skin over their shoulders, and are, in other respects, clothed as decency requires; and even the youngest of the female children have the same covering, which evinces a degree of modesty seldom found amongst untutored people."

In the next stage the skins are roughly cured, cut and fashioned to fit the body. The final mode in the evolution of skin clothing is found among the Eskimo, where such variety as the skins of birds, the pelts of Arctic Hares, and the hides of seals are all used, in special ways for their warmth or water-resisting qualities.

"On the whole, so many skins are available that they (i.e. Eskimo) can afford to be particular in their choice. Seal skin is strong and waterproof; but in very cold weather is not warm enough. Bear skin is exceedingly warm, and one can fall into the water wearing a pair of tied bear-skin trousers without getting wet, but they are tremendously heavy. Musk-ox has the same disadvantage, and it is almost impossible

* This is not quite true. The vapour barrier clothing of recent investigations works on another principle.

to keep the shaggy fur free of blood and dirt. Hare, Eider Duck and fox skins combine great warmth with extreme lightness, but they are all too delicate for general use. Caribou skin is without comparison the best material for clothing in severe cold. It is comparatively strong and also very light and warm, because there is an air-filled cavity in every hair. . . . It may seem strange, but it is in those places in the Eskimo region where the climate is mildest that the greatest variety of garments is needed. There are two reasons for this: first, because only in the outer regions is found the hunting of aquatic animals in open water, which makes very definite demand for waterproof clothing; and second, the purely geographical factor that in the coldest regions the people are already so warmly clad that there is no need for special clothing for ice hunting."—(Birket Smith, *The Eskimos*.)

This need of waterproof clothing has produced what is perhaps the most ingenious garment of all time. In early days the Greenlanders, when whaling, wore a special combination suit of waterproof seal skin, combining hooded anorak, mitts, trousers and boots, all in one piece. The wearer perforce had to enter his protective envelope through a hole in the chest, later tightly closed with draw strings. The same system has been tried again recently in rubberised suits for frogmen.

Another hightly ingenious waterproof garment is worthy of special mention. Until not long ago Aleut hunters and fishermen wore transparent waterproof smocks made from dried, split, seal intestines, sewn edge to edge in spiral fashion.

For the permanent native inhabitants of polar lands such skin clothing is very suitable, but for the active traveller in these places, this form of attire has many disadvantages. It is cumbersome, far too hot and heavy even at very low temperatures when really hard work is done, and womenfolk, with their deft fingers, are essential for its proper care and maintenance over long periods of time. But there has been a recent recrudescence of the use of heavy fur clothing in these modern days of mechanised polar travel. Nylon-pile garments in large degree provide all the best features of fur clothing yet with far less weight and much more strength and durability.

For active polar use another type of clothing has been developed which provides an adequate protection, yet still is light and strong. In parts of China, where biting winds from Central Asia sweep down over the plains, warm clothes have always been required. The Chinaman is no occidental novice in the arts of civilisation. A traditionalist, he retains the fruits of his forefathers' ingenuity, and for ages past he has known the best method of repelling the cold. Well may we Europeans shiver in our thick tweed jackets for, though of the warmest material and of the most handsome cut and colour, our jackets are mere carapaces, divided down the mid-ventral line, held loosely about our persons by two small buttons. The China-man's jacket is longer, reaching half way down his thighs, it is padded and of closely woven almost windproof cloth; with large overlaps, it fastens down the side and reaches upwards to the throat. Ages ago the Chinese realised that it was a wind-proof outer garment, combined with padding, that was most convenient for retaining the stable layer of air around the body. The polar traveller, centuries later, discovered the same thing, and nowadays in his journeys a complete outer covering of windproof material is the normal garb. The garment is made very loose so that there is ample room for movement and for plenty of woollen clothes beneath. It is made in two pieces, trousers and a hooded top which pulls over the head, both being secured tightly at the waist. Often too, in recent times, quilting is combined with windproofing in the old Chinese style.

Underneath the windproofs are worn thick vests and pants, trousers, shirts and sweaters, in whose material the air is held entangled. In this way cooling of the body's surface by moving air is quite prevented. But still there is some loss of heat outward through the garments, for though the thick woollen clothes and the stable air they hold are so good, they are far from being perfect non-conductors.

Even a hundred years ago the clothing needed in active Arctic travel was already apparent, and McClintock, describing the dress used on the 1853-54 expeditions, says:

"Our system of dress is this: soft, warm woollen articles under a cloth which is impenetrable to the wind, and is commonly known as box-cloth; and this again under a suit of closely-textured duck overalls, as snow repellers. The feet are wrapped in squares of blanketing, and covered with leather moccasins during extreme cold; or with duck boots, having leather soles, for moderate Arctic cold, or for wet. The entire suit of clothing in wear weighs from sixteen to twenty-one pounds."

The whole secret of successful cold weather clothing is to keep it dry.* Sweating is the difficulty, because when damp, clothing largely loses its heat insulating properties, and hence the wearer more easily loses his body warmth. Sweating must, therefore, be kept at a minimum, and for this reason the polar traveller or worker must adjust his clothing as far as possible to prevent all chance of overheating.

> "Other distressing circumstances were in operation towards lowering the physical energies of the men . . . while the perspiration caused by the forced work, and which froze upon them on encamping or on standing still for any time, and which the heat of their bodies was not able to thaw was another source of discomfort. The perspiration found its way through the drawers into the lining of the trousers, and the flaps of the duffle trousers were frozen so hard in consequence of the moisture, that we were unable for some days to button them."
>
> (*Arctic Scurvy Committee Report*, 1877.)

It is also relevant that, during strenuous physical work considerable quantities of vitamin C may be lost from the body in the sweat, so perhaps hastening the advent of scurvy.

A new device intended to reduce sweating and its problems was introduced first to the British Army in World War II. This is the string vest† whose advantages quickly became apparent and whose use is almost now a manly fashion. The special feature is that the thick, open mesh keeps the vest at a little distance from the skin so entrapping a satisfactory layer of warm and stable air. When violent exercise is imminent the neck of outer garments may be loosened and then sweat will evaporate freely with the circulating air among the string meshes. Thus the vest and outer garments are saved from moistening with consequent decrease of insulating powers.

Clothing the body in low temperatures is not now difficult, but still the hands and feet are vulnerable and awkward. In the feet the circulation of blood is often poor, while at the same time they are apt to sweat freely. Though the circulation in the

---

* Again, must be mentioned in passing, the exceptional nature of vapour barrier clothing whose future is yet uncertain.

† In the early experimental period a coarser string was used and pants too were worn. They were not a success, particularly on a bicycle, and they were not recommended for Army use.

hands is better and they tend to keep more dry, their suitable covering is made doubly awkward by the fact that their function is to grasp, and that for many necessary little jobs they may have to be wholly or partly exposed. The feet of most of us are not used for grasping once our early days are done; they simply need sufficient protection to keep the soles from chilling on the ice beneath. But this protection from the cold beneath often promotes a general sweating from them when hard work is done. It is usually extremely inconvenient or impossible to alter the coverings of the feet in the course of a day of travelling or labour, and therefore arrangements must be made for the sweat to be absorbed in the least harmful manner. The string vest principle is not conveniently applicable to the feet. On modern polar expeditions, and among civilised peoples who live in cold regions, duffle (or thick blanket cloth) slippers are now used over thick pairs of woollen socks, the outer covering, moccasin, canvas, rubber or other boot being amply large enough. In this way most of the sweat condenses as hoar frost on the outer covering layers, from which it can be scraped off and the duffle later dried. This duffle owes its value to its power of absorbing much moisture without any great loss of its fine insulating properties.

Before 1914 in the 'pioneer' stage of evolution of polar techniques, duffle was little used and reliance was placed upon sennegrass, the dried remains of a Scandinavian bog plant. Because the poverty-stricken primitive Lapp and his wife stuffed their naked toes into reindeer-skin finnesko, lined with sennegrass, it was assumed that civilised explorers, with all the materials of the world at their command, ought to do likewise. Undoubtedly much may be learned from the ways of primitive peoples living under adverse conditions, whether polar or tropical, but lack of means places severe limitations on their inventive genius. For comfort in polar regions the traveller must make an intelligent combination of the methods of life of the primitive peoples who normally live in such places, with the customs and equipment of others more civilised who live under comparable conditions. Much depends upon whether natives are to accompany the travellers.

While it is folly slavishly to follow traditional methods, it is equal folly not to consider carefully the experience and advice of the past, while to imagine one's own methods to be perfection is the most foolish thought of all. Some have thought along other lines:

> "It is only fair to state that so little practical improvement could be effected in the equipment of travelling parties that one cannot reasonably expect that the sledging exploits of 1833 and 1854 will be eclipsed by those of 1875."—(McClintock.)

Of more fundamental difficulty is clothing in the wet-cold climate which often faces the mariner in polar seas or, for example, the dweller on a sub-Antarctic island. Wetness and wind-chill are a formidable pair, and the impermeability needed in the outer layer of clothing to repel the rain is likewise all too apt to retain every particle of sweat.

In these days of mechanisation weight in polar travel is losing its importance, and often the caboose or wannegan, a sturdy little heated home, is tractor-dragged throughout a journey. However, first let us describe the man asleep, then dressing, who travels, in the 'transitional' phase, with his dogs across a polar ice sheet at any date after 1930. He is an Englishman loving peace, simplicity and efficiency, with no patience for unnecessary discomfort nor, or the other hand, any needlessly high standards of comfort and expectation. He sleeps well, eats well and is happy. He lies without moving, warm and comfortable, but being asleep he is not at the moment aware of this. To a stranger it would not at first sight be obvious that there was in fact a man lying there in the tent, for no part of him is visible. On closer inspection, at the far end, he would see an irregular patch of hoar frost on the outer cover of the sleeping-bag, and beneath it a dark cavity between the folds. At the bottom of that cavity is the occupant's nose, and the hoar frost is the condensation of his breath. The man's companion, who is the cook that morning, lights the stove and begins to prepare the breakfast porridge. The man inside the bag allows himself the luxury of a few minutes' wakeful bliss and then, knowing that he must be first outside the tent that day, he begins to dress himself. When he sits up he has already on the greater

number of his clothes, for he has slept in them; they are string
vest (post 1940), thick woollen vest and pants with long arms
and legs, a thick flannel shirt, flannel trousers, a heavy sweater,
and a pair of thick woollen socks. First of all he feels down
inside his sleeping-bag and fishes out from the region of his
knees the mitts and footgear, warm and soft, that he wore the
previous day and which were dried over the stove during the
evening meal. Then, sitting on his bag, he takes off the socks
he has been wearing for the night and puts on another pair,
into which he tucks the ends of his pants and trousers. Over
the first pair he at once pulls on another pair of larger socks,
then a pair of duffle slippers, then another pair of duffle slippers.
His mocassins or boots meanwhile have been having a final dry
against the stove. Now he puts them on and ties them, carefully
arranging the tongue and flaps so as to leave no gaps through
which soft snow or drift may creep. That done, he takes the
plate of porridge that his comrade passes to him, melts some
lumps of butter upon it, and eats in grateful silence.

The porridge finished and the plate scraped clean, he drains
his mug of tea. His windproof outer garments have been his
pillow for the night. First he shakes out the trousers, puts
them on as he sits, and ties their ends tightly round his ankles
outside his boots. He makes snug his neck with a large silk
handkerchief. Then he pulls his windproof blouse over his
head, tucks its lower edge inside his trousers and ties the draw-
string, a piece of lampwick. Perhaps he is more up to date and
zip fasteners allow dressing with less contortions. He is now
nearly ready for the outside world, so next he rolls up his
sleeping-bag and ties it fast. He buckles round his waist his
belt and knife, pulls on a pair of wristlets and arranges his
windproof hood and balaclava helmet in the fashion which will
best suit the day. He has then only to make ready his goggles,
put on his inner and outer mitts, untie the door-sleeve, and
there he is, ready to squeeze through to the outside world and
greet his dogs, or perhaps his 'weasel.'

The portrayal of evolutionary change is commonly convenient by describing a number of isolated occasions, circumstances or species. So it is with the evolution of polar travel:

some glimpses may suffice. Travel by man-hauling 'pioneer' stage Englishmen in Antarctica before the first World War, may be compared with the experiences of their dog-efficient, 'transitional' stage, sons twenty years later under like climatic circumstances.

Scott wrote (in 1905) as follows in *The Voyage of the Discovery:*

". . . now we can see well to put on our marching boots. It is very trying work. With a caution born of experience we took immense care last night in freezing them to conform as nearly as possible to the shape of the feet. After the march they had been wet through, and came off in a soft and flabby condition; we knew that this would only last for a few minutes, and as they froze we had carefully supported them and kneaded them into the required shape. Half an hour later they were so hard that we could throw them about without risk of altering them. . . . We squat down and withdraw on foot from its night clothing, grope in our breast for our day-socks, produce one still very wet but moderately warm, jam our foot into it, and with many gasps proceed to wedge it into a wooden finnesko. The finnesko has been prepared by placing in it a sole cut from reindeer skin and a little padding of sennegrass. The grass is soft, but the sole wooden as the boot, and has need of much pushing to get it into place. We are lucky if our foot gets half way into its rocky cover at the first attempt. We leave it at that for the moment, and proceed with the other; by the time it is in a similar position, an inch can be gained on the first, and so inch by inch these tiresome boots are pulled on. Meanwhile our feet have got alarmingly cold, and with a groan we are obliged to start up and stamp them.

There is no exaggeration in the above picture. The putting on of our finneskoes in very cold weather was generally a matter of excruciating agony: it often brought tears to the eyes and always strong expressions to the lips, and all this with footwear that on board the ship could be put on as easily as one's hat. Yet even when one was fuming in discomfort, a glance at one's writhing companions made it impossible not to appreciate the humorous side of the situation, and we have often paused in the midst of our trying labours to indulge in a real hearty laugh.

Heaven help the man who had failed in caution on the previous night! At first, from want of experience, and later from carelessness or by accident, a boot would be found in the morning squeezed flat and frozen hard in that impossible shape. There was nothing for the owner to do but to thaw it into shape with his foot, which had to be withdrawn at intervals and rubbed violently to restore the circulation. The least time in which one could hope to cope with a boot of this description was half an hour."

Cherry-Garrard wrote likewise of the 'pioneer' phase in his *The Worst Journey in the World:*

"The trouble is sweat and breath. I never knew before how much of the body's waste comes out through the pores of the skin. On the most bitter days, when we had to camp before we had done a four-hour march, in order to nurse back our frozen feet, it seemed that we must be sweating. And all this sweat, instead of passing away through the porous wool of our clothing and gradually drying off us, froze and accumulated. It passed just away from our flesh and then became ice; we shook plenty of snow and ice down from inside our trousers every time we changed our foot-gear, and we could have shaken it from our vests and from between our vests and shirts, but of course we could not strip to this extent. But when we got into our sleeping-bags, if we were fortunate, we became warm enough during the night to thaw this ice; part remained in our clothes, part passed into the skins of our sleeping-bags, and soon both were sheets of armour plate."

Thus, day by day, more body heat was wasted and more wretched did the men become. All that was needed was an increased supply of paraffin so that some could be used to dry clothing and equipment each evening in the tent. But more paraffin meant a greater load to be dragged by tired legs. The loads of man-haulers were cut down to the barest minimum, the weight of paraffin taken being just enough to melt the ice for drink and to heat the food. No allowance was included for mere warmth and drying of clothes. In those days, too, the Nansen cooker was popular, an ingenious device used with the Primus stove, and designed to shut in every particle of heat to speed the preparation of the food.

With dog transport came the ability to use just those small extra quantities of paraffin essential for the drying of clothes and sleeping bags for the maintenance of their insulation at its best, and so for comparative comfort, sound sleep, happiness and efficiency. That was the basis of the change to the 'transitional' phase. Think of two men with their dog teams making camp and resting for the night. The largest and most obvious item of camp equipment is the tent itself. This has been designed to stand firm against all winds, however great their strength, and to keep out the drifting particles of snow. It must also be light in weight, simply and rapidly erected under any conditions. It is made normally to house two men, but will take three or even four if necessary. The tent complete is about 50 lb. in weight, and pyramidal in form. It is almost 7 ft. high at the apex, and the base is about 7 ft. square. The walls are double and of thin windproof material. One-piece bamboo poles are permanently but loosely jointed together at the apex, and from them the inner cover is suspended. The outer cover is thrown over the whole so that the two layers of cloth are separated by a space of about 6 in. This space or layer of relatively stagnant air gives insulation from the cold. Close to the apex is a small ventilator in the form of a bamboo tube. The doorway is of the sleeve type usual in polar tents, capable of being bunched together and tightly tied from within or without. The outer cover has a skirt all round that lies flat upon the ground. On this boxes and snow are piled to hold fast the whole, and there is a guy-rope from the centre of each side. Likewise the inner tent has an inwardly projecting skirt that makes for snugness. The tent as a whole somewhat resembles a limpet (but square instead of oval), clinging stoutly to the rocks despite the buffetings of the waves. Similarly, the wind beating on the sides of the tent has a resultant downward force, tending to press it more firmly to the ice. It is only when too few boxes or too little snow are piled upon the tent skirt that such tents can be overturned.

Now imagine these two 'transitional' phase men, after a long day's sledging, making camp for the night. First the dogs are fed, each with its 1 lb. lump of pemmican, and the sledges unlashed. Then, while the dogs are licking up the crumbs, the men can set about the erection of the tent. Together they spread the legs from which already hangs the inner cover. Then, seizing the outer cover, with the deftness of practice, they throw it over the whole and quickly place upon its skirt the heavy boxes lying ready in a circle. The tent now roughly secured, they settle their dogs for the night. Some are already asleep. Those that perhaps may chew their harness must be tethered otherwise, or freed according to their individual requirements. That done, in goes one man into the tent, and he receives the skins and sleeping-bags, the food box and the personal bags which the other passes to him. The outside man heaps snow round the boxes on the tent skirt, fills the cooking pots with ice and arranges all things with care so that on the morrow the start will not be delayed. He must know exactly the position of every box and bag, every ski and ice-axe, so that if all is drifted over in the night unnecessary digging will be avoided. Then, satisfied that all is secure outside, after a final glance at the dogs now peacefully curled up beside the sledge, he places the spade within easy reach and worms his way through the narrow entrance.

His trailing legs and feet are in an icy land many degrees below zero, the wind billowing and tugging at his windproof trousers. But his head and shoulders are in a climate that might be half the world away, warm and dry and seeming quiet, the cheerful roar of the Primus stove drowning the noise of the wind outside. The companion of the day's labours is already there, seated upon his unrolled sleeping-bag, stirring the pemmican heating on the stove. The man draws in his legs, ties the entrance tightly behind him and is at home. The cook sits among his household gods on one side; on the other is a dry and glossy reindeer skin, a bag of personal clothes and oddments at its head, and the second sleeping-bag, all ready to be spread. In the corner by the entrance the ground-sheet is turned back. All the newcomer has to do is to squat in this corner, carefully brush the snow from his clothes, remove his moccasins or boots and scrape the ice from their inside, then replace the corner of the ground-sheet, hang up his mitts and duffles, footgear and headgear, and his windproofs in the apex of the tent, unroll his sleeping-bag and lie at ease upon it. The ice is already melted in the pot, and the main meal of the day is almost ready. Appetising odours fill the tent, and weary limbs relax. Mouths water, just as did the saliva drip from the mouths of the impatient dogs outside. First an orange drink that wards off scurvy and partially quenches thirst, and then come the plates of pemmican that will do much to satisfy their hunger. So they have supper peacefully in their little home, spend the evening talking, sewing and mending harnesses, perhaps reading for a while by candlelight before snuggling into warm eiderdown sleeping-bags. Then, the stove at last put out, they drop into a peaceful sleep that will last eight hours before they start the next day's work.

Those of the past had struggled gamely on, dragging their

sledges, their aching bodies more and more weary, their clothing daily more clogged with ice, which at night must be melted by the heat of their bodies in the frozen bags before they could fall into a damp uneasy slumber. It is marvellous that the heroes of the old 'pioneer' phase had courage and resolution enough to force themselves onwards, gnawed by dreadful hunger, and continually threatened by scurvy. For their 'transitional' stage sons it is or was all so different that the imagination must stretch to the full to understand the conditions of the past. In Cherry-Garrard's words *The Worse Journey in the World:* "The day's march was bliss compared with the night's rest, and both were awful. . . . I do not believe that any man, however sick he is, has a much worse time than we had in those bags, shaking with cold until our backs would almost break. . . ." With dog-drawn sledges more paraffin is taken and the Nansen cooker is now obsolete. The naked Primus flame cheers and warms the men as it cooks their food, and dries their clothing, duffles and mitts hanging above in the top of the tent, or disposed in a close circle at the foot of the stove itself. Then, in the morning, the stove is lit once more and, before cooking the breakfast porridge, is allowed to roar away unchecked, drying off the condensation of the sleepers' breath, the crystal flakes that hang inside the tent.

The advent of mechanised transport in the 'modern' stage has been accompanied by the growing use of a caboose or wannegan, a house built upon a sledge. It is a caravan, ready, warm and comfortable. The day's journey may reach three figures, the variety of seismic or other equipment may be astonishing by the scientific standards of the past, and the overall complexity and cost will be great. Work can now be done, loads hauled, and journeys attempted which without mechanisation were quite impossible. Yet those who have travelled skilfully with dogs may fail to find the same contentment of spirit in their wannegan, though admitting its great convenience and other special attributes. Noise and smell are ill companions for long.

Objectives must be achieved, and by the most advantageous means that resources will allow. But there is little doubt that desires for high standards of comfort and food are sometimes now allowed to have an influence which to an earlier generation of polar travellers must seem unnecessarily complicated and costly. The minimum diet for personal efficiency in polar travel has been achieved for thirty years: to exceed the basic need is symptomatic of our times.

Even today dog transport still has, and will have, its special uses and occasions. So let us turn once more to detail, stores, food, aspiration and effort, the beginning of a coastwise Antarctic journey in 'transitional' style whether in fact before or after World War II.

Most of what they take is standard. One pound of pemmican every day for each dog, and a man ration of about $1\frac{3}{4}$ lb. They decide that though there are only three of them it will be best to take two tents, each of which is made for two. The maps must be partly plotted nightly in the tent, and they believe that to leave room for this and to avoid overcrowding inside the tent and loss of speed in morning preparations, will compensate for the added weight that must be carried. Nine weeks' fuel for two tents means taking nine two-gallon tins of paraffin, and they wish they knew of some containers as strong and as durable, yet very greatly less in weight. Two sets of cooking pots, two stoves and spares, a mug, a plate and a spoon for each is the total of their domestic equipment. Then, besides for each man a down sleeping-bag, a reindeer floorskin, a small bag of spare clothes, mending materials and a book, there must be a shovel for each tent, spare cloth for tent repairs, a tool kit and a medical box. There must be a spare trace and harness for each dog, and bits of rope and canvas, a climbing rope, 100 feet of lash line for each sledge, candles, matches, spirit for starting the stoves, and an ice-axe and a pair of skis for each man. As well, knowing that the surfaces will be very variable and that sometimes the temperature may rise unpleasantly near to freezing point, they take a pair of snow-shoes each. Besides all these there are notebooks, pencils, theodolite and tripod, cameras, binoculars and geological hammers. They realise too that they have an opportunity to make a small controlled experiment, so they cut special lumps of pure seal blubber, weighing 1 lb. each, and these they will feed once a week in

ICEBERG

(Photographs by courtesy of the National Institute of Oceanography)
(From Illustrated Ice Glossary in "Polar Record")

TABULAR BERG

Maudheim under snow, 12th November, 1950. The huts are nearly submerged beneath a single, smooth snowdrift. The prevailing wind blows from right to left of the photograph. Though the ridge of each hut was almost 4 m. above the snow surface when the base was established in February, 1950, it was less than 1 m. above when the photograph was taken 9 months later. The depth of snow which accumulated over the same period on an unobstructed level surface nearby was only 50 cm.

(Photograph by C. W. M. Swithinbank, "Norwegian–British–Swedish Antarctic Expedition, 1949-52.")

place of pemmican to one team of dogs, to see if there is any difference in their final condition when the work is done.

Thus the three men plan and collect their equipment and stores, checking over all they need, and never taking the contents of any box or can for granted without themselves seeing that it really is so. They examine the sledges with great care and assure themselves that all is as it should be. They pinch and scrape and refuse to take anything that is not absolutely essential, but even so find that for their nine weeks' journey there are 3,600 lb. of load if they are to bring back all their dogs alive, as they know they must on this occasion. There must be 1,200 lb. on each sledge; that is 120 lb. per dog; but they know too that the loads will diminish by some 12 lb. each sledge each day, and so they hope for good surfaces at the start that they may go on without relaying.

At last the day to start has arrived, and thankfully the three men welcome it, for to be at work is always better than merely to prepare. They have searched the tents and mended every tiny hole, their clothes are warm and sound, their dog harnesses are all in good condition, and they have checked and re-checked every item of equipment. They rest in the assurance that no essential want is left behind. The night before the dogs received their last full meal of seal meat, and now they seem as anxious as the men to go. A few other men that day are at hand to help them off. The three sledges have not been loaded overnight for their runners need scraping before the start, but the boxes of dog and man food stand in ready piles. The three sledges are loaded some little way apart from one another. First, two layers each of nine 50-lb. boxes, then on top, in bags, the tent, sleeping-bag, floorskin and spare harnesses. The lash line is passed round and round in a special way so that it can be quickly tightened, and at the ends is fastened in a fashion that can be jerked undone with ease. At the back of the sledge, on the handle-bars, goes a bag that can be opened on the way, containing camera, binoculars, lunch, spare mitts and little oddments like string and bits of chewing gum. Tucked in on top, and readily to hand on the second sledge is the coil of climbing rope, for use in an emergency. Fastened to the tail

D

end of the hindmost sledge is a wheel that counts the miles, while on the leading sledge is the navigating compass.

Now the sledges are lashed and ready, and it is time to harness the dogs and get them to their places. They know that more is afoot than a short day's run to fetch in seals, and are consequently the more excited. Eventually all three sledges are complete, and the dogs lie, their traces taut, with ears pricked up and whining to be off. Some of the young dogs leap to their feet and jump wildly in the air until suppressed. Finally, the men put on their skis, then move up to the front of each sledge to help the start, for with the heavy load the dogs cannot move it of themselves. The driver of the leading sledge at last orders up his team, and at once the babble starts. There are a few moments of wild excitement, the animals make impatient little rushes forward only to be stopped short at their trace ends, they yowl and whine and stand up on their hind legs all eagerness to go. The driver with his left hand hauls in a foot of the main trace, then lets go, shouts the command to start and jerks the front of the sledge with his right hand, and they are off. He jumps straight his skis, grabs the sledge and away they go, bouncing over the tide crack on to the sea-ice of the bay, where they gallop the first few hundred yards until the heavy load begins to tell.

So the three men start across the hard-crusted surface in the clear sunshine of the day. Away they go into the unknown, to sweat and labour in the cold, the three of them and their thirty dogs, dependent on themselves alone, their strength, their wits, and their courage. They go to discover what is new, they will see what men have never seen before, and all in a land that is filled with peace.

As a tail-piece let us make comparison with life at a strategic polar airbase, a new metropolis of men, noise, heat and mechanics, the very essence of the 'modern' stage and way of life. The population is partly service and partly civilian, some thousands of each, and not a woman among them. In the brief summer weeks they work prodigiously, in eight hour shifts around the clock, and likewise meals and wages are prodigious too. Great bull-dozers move moraines and form

the airstrip, and aircraft come and go each hour. Ships by the
score, freighters, tankers and naval vessels, moor by the new
built jetties, unload mechanically and are away to give place for
more. Huge oil tanks store the liquid fuel for engines and for
furnaces. Live steam is piped throughout the township in steel
ducts, glass-wool insulated, for to be indoors at less than 70° F.
is seemingly to suffer. Wood and metal barracks, stores,
hangars, cinemas, offices, mess rooms, everything, stretch out
upon the moraines of this polar desert with the icecap rising in
the clouds behind. Trucks rush down the rocky streets; bustle,
noise, efficiency and discipline rule the days and nights continu-
ously. Men are aware of their coming money, their fancied
hardships, their lack of women, their need for newer films.
Quiet, solitude, serenity, polar animals and plants are absent.
Only in the distant view of sea, of hills, of ice and sky, is there
something left of the peace which once prevailed.

CHAPTER IV

Dogs

THE advent of efficient mechanical transport for use in polar
lands has greatly diminished the importance of the dog. Yet
dog transport still has special features of value and at times may
be indispensable. In any event as our oldest domestic animal
we have a sympathy and a desire to understand dogs and their
use, and this study too helps in the interpretation of polar
history. Even today in the most mechanical of polar enterprises
dogs still have their place: they have therapeutic value when all
else has become redundant.

A pup, unsteady on its childish legs, has always been beloved
of little boys and girls, and that no doubt was why primitive
man brought the little animal home to his children in the cave.
Despite the teasing which would only serve to sharpen its wits,
the puppy must have survived and flourished, and begun to kill
small animals and birds that the children could not catch themselves. In such a way perhaps the original ancestors of the dog
came to be man's first domestic animals, his servants, not his
guests, like cats. The precise ancestry of our dogs is still in
dispute, but probably they derived from several species and

sub-species of dog-like creatures among which the wolf was one. Probably the domestication took place on more than one occasion and in several different places, and certainly in some instances there has been a later mixing with other dog-like forms. This plastic material in human hands has been bred by selection into the many kinds, now called varieties, which are all recognised still as 'dogs,' some useful, some fantastic, of all shapes and sizes from the King Charles' spaniel to the saluki, from the elkhound to the dachshund, and from the barkless dog of central Africa to the hairless dog of Mexico. This selection was started at an extremely early period; and centuries B.C. there are Chinese descriptions of methods of cooking the chow and of garnishing its body for the table, and mural paintings in Egypt depict scenes of hunting the gazelle with dogs hardly different from the Afghan hounds of today. Since then, selection has given rise to all the kinds to be seen at Cruft's, and to others not yet recognised. The one type out of all these that is concerned in polar work goes under the general title of 'husky,' and is primarily kept for hauling sledges.

Working huskies are to be seen at their best in Greenland, Alaska and Canada; and in this last decade in the Falkland Islands Dependencies in Antarctica. The Samoyed of northern Asia is a somewhat similar but less fine animal. There is little doubt that the husky is more closely related to the wolf than are most of the other domestic breeds. Indeed, in Canada, husky bitches are sometimes tied to trees in the wild so that a wolf may father their pups, this crossing with the wolf being held to give added stamina to the breed.

The reputation of huskies for extreme savagery is an ill-founded belief, based, with few exceptions, on their behaviour in North America when hunting for themselves and near starvation in summer, their native or half-breed masters being unable or unwilling to provide food when the animals are not at work. When these dogs are well-fed and cared for by white men, though still savage among themselves, they are friendly and lovable. Under the conditions of an expedition they will almost never bite a man, except perhaps by accident as when being separated in their private quarrels. It is unlikely that, however well one knew them, there would be no bitten fingers were fifty or sixty ordinary English dogs, bulldogs, terriers, spaniels, seized rapidly one after the other by the hair of the neck and back, jerked off their feet, swung through a half-circle and over a small ship's side, to be caught by another man waiting in a boat below. Yet, normally, with one's own huskies such operations pass without incident.

The social behaviour of these dogs when together in large numbers is both interesting and peculiar, and in certain respects resembles that of their human masters. There are steadfast friends and implacable enemies, faithful bitches and flirting bitches, dogs with a favourite bitch, and regular Don Juans pursuing all the ladies. When settled round their owner's home they live in groups, usually families, sometimes associations of friends; sometimes a dozen or more together, the offspring of a single bitch, or again it may be two lonely dogs that have become friendly in their friendlessness. Each such group attempts to maintain a territory in which it lives, and from which all outside intruders are driven. For the dogs these territories are clearly defined, and two groups may for long stand growling defiance at one another a few feet apart, not coming to grips until one, through folly or of set purpose goes too far, and then at once a general fight ensues. In such fights friends will valiantly help each other, and it is a bitter life for the dog that can rely on none. In each group one dog is usually dominant, a king who has ascended to his position of authority entirely by his own prowess, and only by it does he continue to reign. An aged king may rule by bluff some time after he cannot really hold his own, purely because his bluff is sufficient to prevent the younger dogs from hazarding a trial of strength. When two meet, the one that growls and bares his teeth is the inferior, and he knows it. The dominant dog just looks silently and exerts his personality, and then perhaps makes a sudden rush, bowls his adversary over upon his back, and stands on top of him while the vanquished howls for mercy.

Post-war expedition practice in the 'modern' phase, notably for example in the British Falkland Islands Dependencies Survey, is to keep the dogs at all times tethered, even at bases and permanent stations. This practice obviates no doubt much fighting which in any event is mostly harmless, and has other advantages in regard to time and routine. But this 'spanning' of dogs has perhaps the disadvantage that there is less opportunity for the dogs themselves to develop their natural 'pecking order,' much interest is lost to the observer, and the dogs in general keep less fit and clean.

The rest of this chapter is partly descriptive and partly historical. It covers something of the technique of dog driving but, in addition, recounts with the aid of quotations, something of the outworn disputes between those of our fathers' generation who had to be convinced that dog transport in Antarctica was more efficient than haulage by men. There is still interest here, if only in accentuating more clearly than ever the immense evolution in polar technique in the last forty years. Considerable quotations are made from the earlier version of this present book, written in the late thirties, when the old disputation did still seem largely relevant.

In England by law it is forbidden to use dogs for haulage or for pack carrying. They may not be used to help the pedlar with his barrow as in Brittany and Belgium. The man must use his own legs or keep a donkey or a goat. An exception is made to allow the retrievers and setters that bear big, brightly polished money boxes upon their backs at the London railway stations. This unfamiliarity with the use of dogs for haulage played an unconscious part in promoting the view so common in England in earlier years of this century, that Englishmen could not efficiently drive dogs on polar expeditions, particularly in the Antarctic. For Scandinavians it was different; they were, supposedly, brought up driving dogs and wearing skis. The fact that people from England were using dogs for their normal winter transport in northern Canada and Labrador seemed to be forgotten. In England itself there was a deep-rooted conviction that the use of dogs as transport animals was cruel. Gentlemen used horses.

The dependence upon British sailors, instead of dogs, for hauling sledges, arose from those many Franklin search-expeditions which did so much to open the Canadian Arctic archipelago, and this dependence continued when attention was transferred to the Antarctic. The sailors did wonderful things, but their achievements might have been still more splendid had they regularly used dogs to help them. It is a strange fact that out of all the British 'pioneer' stage Antarctic expeditions before the first World War, although some took a few dogs for subsidiary use, the members of the expeditions who had seen dogs properly driven in northern countries and could appreciate their value could be counted on the fingers of one hand. This earlier attitude is well brought out in a passage from Hugh Robert Mill's biography of Shackleton:

> "On the 7th the captain (Scott) called Shackleton into his cabin and gave him charge of the dogs in view of the great southern journey. No one on board had any special experience of dog-driving, and the captain had devised special harness for the teams. Now Shackleton was set the task, in no way alarming to a British sailor, of discovering by his own efforts in a week or two the art that takes a northern Canadian years of apprenticeship to master. The result was better than one could have expected; but it served to strengthen the fine old British tradition which Sir Clements Markham set such store by, that the best polar draught animals are the human members of the expedition. And in their hearts the *Discovery* people did not believe in dogs."

The words of McClintock (quoted in the *Antarctic Manual*), had been forgotten:

> "In the Government searching Expedition we gained no experience of snow-houses, and but little of sledging with dogs, yet that little was sufficient to convince us of their value. For instance, during the spring of 1854, our only team of dogs was kept constantly at work, and, without counting occasional short trips, they accomplished in sixty days' travelling 1,830 miles, affording an average rate of thirty miles, their sledge on the whole being rather lightly laden. On several occasions they performed the distance of sixty miles between the *Assistance* and the *North Star* in from twenty to twenty-four hours."

McClintock made these statements, even though his methods of driving were clearly not of the best:

> "When a dog feels the lash he usually bites his neighbour, who bites the next dog, and a general fight and howling began. The lash is no longer of any avail, and the driver is compelled to restore order with the handle of the whip. The journey is then more briskly continued, and so on throughout the march, until at length camping time comes."

When Shackleton sailed in the *Endurance* in 1914, his was the first British expedition to set out with the intention of relying on dogs for haulage. But let us not criticise the past in the light of the experience that we now possess, experience which is the past's legacy to us.* To use the words of a writer of the twelfth century:

> "We are like dwarfs, sitting on the shoulders of giants, in order that we may see things more numerous and more distant than they could see, not, certainly, by reason of the sharpness of our own vision or the tallness of our bodies, but because we are lifted and raised on high by the greatness of the giants."

But criticism is legitimate whenever the knowledge available at the time has not been or is not used to the full.

This is not the place for a detailed description of the intricate technique of dog driving. For that a writer of extremely wide experience would be needed, a man who had seen dogs at work and had himself driven in east and west Greenland, Canada, Alaska and Arctic Eurasia, and Antarctica besides, and could thereby properly estimate the true worth of each. But a brief account of certain points may be of interest. The size of a team of dogs varies from five, which is a common number in Canada, to fifteen, which is as many as can conveniently be managed. As many as fifteen would only be used in quite exceptional circumstances for a particularly heavy piece of haulage, or on an expedition where some are to be killed before the end of a long journey. In Labrador fewer than five dogs was and may still be quite common, the man often pulling alongside his dogs. The dogs of a team should so far as possible be the members of a single group, as already described, since in that way there is less quarrelling and each dog can feel happy among friends. Entire males are normally used, though in parts of Eurasia castrated animals used to be considered to be more efficient. Commonly, one or more bitches is included in the team, as their presence enlivens the dogs, and more than

* To gain an appreciation of the thoroughness with which a previous generation investigated the difficulties of Arctic travel, reference should be made to a work such as the "Report of the Committee appointed by the Lords Commissioners of the Admiralty, to enquire into the Causes of the Outbreak of Scurvy in the recent Arctic Expedition; the Adequacy of the Provision made by the Admiralty in the Way of Food and Medical Comforts; and the propriety of the Orders given by the Commander of the Expedition for Provisioning the Sledge Parties, 1877."

compensates for their smaller size and weaker pull. Some drivers make it a practice always to have a bitch in the lead, believing the bitches to be more intelligent than the dogs. Another advantage of a bitch is that her pups may easily be drafted into the team, and the young dogs are more easily trained by running them alongside their mother. Some men begin the training of the pups at an astonishingly early age, but usually training starts at eight or nine months old, and soon after a year old they should have filled out and become really hard-working dogs. The young soon learn to pull, and some pups put into harness for the first time alongside their mother will pull from the initial word of command. The age at which a dog is in its prime as a traction animal is probably at about three years old, though some would put it at a higher figure. As a general rule the younger dog has the greater speed and as strong a pull at the beginning of the day and on good going, while the older animal tends to haul more steadily and continues to do so when the surfaces are bad.

The arrangement of the dogs and their harness when at work varies with the country, according to what is considered to be the best in the local conditions, though, as in so much else, conservatism plays a large part. An example of a native-made piece of equipment, which is by no means the best that local means allow, comes from Siberia. There one tribe by tradition drove its dogs in a barbarous form of lion harness, a most cruel and inefficient device.

As for the arrangement of the dog team, in some places each dog has its own trace, all being rather short and equal in length so that the dogs pull in fan formation some 15 ft. in front of the sledge. Elsewhere the dogs are driven tandem, each pulling in a stiff shoulder collar rather than a close-fitting and pliable seal-skin, lampwick, or rope harness, and a pair of traces runs down the two sides to which each dog's collar is attached and between which they run. Alternatively, the dogs may be driven each on a separate trace, but all the traces of different lengths, the leading dog being even as much as 25 yards in front of the sledge. But whatever the arrangement of the team, the object is the same, to drag the sledge load as quickly as may be from one place to another. It is the variable nature of the intervening country which should determine the method in which the team is arranged to do its work. There are several contrary factors in the possible arrangement of the dogs. Within reason, the further the dogs are from the sledge the more easily can the dogs or sledge be manoeuvred separately over and around obstacles, but the longer the traces the less control can the driver exert from his position by the sledge. Another factor is that dogs prefer to run together in a bunch, but were they allowed to do so they clearly could not all pull efficiently. The nearest approach towards the 'bunch' that is feasible is to drive in fan formation with all the dogs on equal traces. From the point of view of the dogs' good spirits this is doubtless the best method, but it has the great disadvantage that in heavy going each dog has the added effort of making its own individual trail, and there is always a tendency for one to try and fall in behind another, and so use the trail already made. At the same time there is some waste of effort, the pull from the outer dogs being partly sideways. At the opposite extreme is the driving of the dogs in single file, either on a continuous or on separate traces: the work is more lonely for the individual animal, but each is spared the wasteful effort of making a separate trail. In this case, however, a specially trained leading dog is needed, an animal of sturdy disposition which is willing to run or plod ahead, to set the pace and show the way to those behind. To get the best results it is necessary to devise the most efficient combination of these factors for the actual country to be traversed. Though at first the dogs, being used to one driving formation, may be a little upset by a change of method, this soon passes, and there is no reason why the mode of driving should not be changed in the course of an exploratory journey if a change of surface conditions demands it.

To travel quickly it is essential to maintain the spirit of the dogs. There is little difficulty where the dogs are used between settlements and scattered houses and the journeys are short, but it is very different on polar exploratory expeditions where the journeys may extend over many weeks and cover many hundreds of miles, with no feature of interest to the dogs. Much of the art of dog driving lies in following the middle way between too great and dispiriting chastisement for natural canine wilfulness, and too little insistence upon absolute obedience to the words of command.

The normal diet for a dog nowadays on an extended journey is one pound of dog pemmican per day. This seems to be enough to provide the dog's energy requirements, down to moderately low temperatures, but it is by no means sufficient to appease the hunger. It is only in the last few years that properly controlled experiments on dogs under actual working conditions have been initiated taking into account both dietary requirements and actual, measured work done. We have long known that dogs cannot get scurvy through lack of vitamin C in the diet, for they differ completely from man in being able to manufacture it in their own bodies. The vitamin requirements of different species of animals are by no means necessarily the same. Anyone who has seen dogs working on a journey must be left with a feeling of amazement and wonder at their perfection. Beyond a quantity of snow, each day each dog absorbs a single pound of fat and protein, and in exchange provides a marvellous abundance of energy. They pull the sledge, they sleep out the blizzards unprotected, and they will work themselves to the end, all in return for a lump of pemmican and man's care and friendship.

In this mechanical 'modern' age it may at first thought seem redundant to continue into the discussion of the relative merits of dogs and men as haulage animals. But in the pre-motor era it was so live an issue, more particularly in British Antarctic endeavour, that some little consideration now has still a residual worth. It is not the present object to revive past controversy. Further, it is important to realise that the method of traction which is clearly the most efficient in one set of circumstances may be far from the best in an entirely different set of conditions, and that both sets of conditions may well occur in the course of a single polar expedition. This certainly was more true than some appreciated at the time; and it remains true today for there are still circumstances where haulage by dogs or men is a direct choice and mechanical haulage is in no way relevant. Crevassed mountain areas afford examples, though sometimes now the helicopter provides a better answer still.

Dipping then back into the past Scott, writing in 1905, in the 'pioneer' period, remarked "whatever the sledge traveller's objectives may be, it is obvious that they are best achieved by speed on the march; and hence, where conditions are equal, speed and the distance travelled are a direct gauge of the efficiency of sledging preparations and the spirit of those who undertake this arduous service." With this speed there was of course implied the ability to remain long periods unsupported in the field, the longer the period the greater the efficiency. It is now generally agreed that in most circumstances where straightforward travelling is possible, dogs are more efficient as traction animals than men. That is to say, that under good conditions a team of dogs can travel a greater distance than a team of men, depending only on the food they carry with them on the sledge.

Beyond this there is the further point brought out by Scott when he remarked, "broadly speaking, there are two ways in which dogs may be used, they may be taken with the idea of bringing them all back safe and sound, or they may be treated as pawns in the game, regardless of their lives." Obviously the second method is the more efficient, since as day by day the loads diminish, less tractive power is needed, and then the food remaining can with advantage be divided among the smaller number of hungry mouths. "The avoidance of unnecessary pain should be the aim, and suddenly and painlessly to end the life of an animal which has been well fed and well cared for is not cruelty."

In the past, owing to ignorance of the food requirements of dogs and lack of experience in driving them, many Englishmen revolted against such use of dogs. Scott voiced the ideas of many when he wrote what then appeared to be the truth: "To say that they (i. e. the dogs) do not greatly increase the radius of action is absurd; to pretend that they can be worked to this end without pain, suffering and death is equally futile." But later improvements in rationing and technique allow of dogs being used without cruelty for extended sledge journeys. Still, even today there can be few who enjoy killing dogs, least of all the man who for weeks on end has daily driven them, cheering on his team with a steady torrent of endearments and epithets, the man who has fed them and attended to their every need, and has perhaps handled them daily since they were pupped. That man hates to kill his dogs, it is as the murder of friends, but when forced to do so he does it with all possible kindliness and speed. It was surely better, in the 'transitional' phase, that the exploration of the polar regions should be advanced by the instant death of a few well-loved and faithful dogs, free from apprehensions until the end as we believe, and no more hungry than their masters. On the other hand, the slower, less efficient, method of man-hauling in the 'pioneer' stage was surely more harsh, the sensitive and self-conscious mind of man being ever a prey to mental fear just as his over-strained body was the constant seat of pains and hunger.

Experience seems to suggest that the most advantageous results are to be obtained when the load upon the sledge is such that each dog pulls about 100 lb., though recent advances in the use of low friction sledge runners might markedly increase these figures. Thus, a team of ten dogs appears to give their best (as measured in lb.-miles) if they drag a sledge load of about 1,000 lb. On really good surfaces much more may be attempted, but all things considered, for a journey where soft snow may force the teams to relay, about 100 lb. per dog seems likely to give the greatest range. In contrast, those whose experience of man-hauling is greatest, have given it as their opinion that a load of somewhat more than 200 lb. per man is the most that can with advantage be attempted. The conclusion from experience is that a man working at his greatest efficiency will pull rather more than twice as much as a dog at its best, while daily eating a little less that twice as much, but travelling not quite so far.

Now compare five men, as they drag their burden of 1,000 lb. across the snow, with a team of ten dogs pulling a similar load alongside. On most surfaces the dogs will go further in the day, owing to their greater speed during the first few hours. Later in the day both men and dogs will be more nearly equal in their speed. On any surface, a track made by a previous sledge is of some assistance to a team of dogs, which always prefer to follow where others have led the way. Though the trail itself may make no difference in easing the work their legs must do, yet they are always cheered by its presence and increase their speed. With men, the value of a track is more often measured by the amount of pull they must exert, a physical rather than a mental criterion.

It may happen that the surface of the snow, crusted by wind or thaw, will break at every step. This is wearying in the extreme for both men and dogs. A man will normally break through somewhat more easily, but if he is wearing skis or snow-shoes, then he has a great advantage over the dog. But on a surface that is very irregular, such as broken or contorted sea ice or sastrugi, though it is hard and withstands the feet of men and dogs alike, the dogs, being four-footed, have a marked advantage. The unevenness in the surface will always cause an inequality in the pull upon the traces, making it difficult to keep the sledge in motion. Here the dogs, being more numerous, are better placed than men, for they will distribute the strain more evenly.

This comparison between dogs and men in their ability to drag a sledge can be carried further, to time as well as place. In some polar lands there are many days of uniformly clouded skies, when a dim grey light pervades the world, so that ice and sky seem merged in one, when up and down, hillocks and pits are alike invisible, and obstacles are not seen till almost touched. Then the dogs are once more at a great advantage, stepping along as always, with waving tails and lolling tongues, while the men grope their way slowly forward, peering ahead with anxious eyes and at intervals falling, despite their care. But dogs are less efficient than men on those days when a fresh head-wind blows, carrying with it a fierce low drift, perhaps barely reaching to knee-height. Then men can step out little hindered, but it may be almost impossible to urge a team of dogs to face it. The flying particles of drift fill their nostrils, clog their eyes and make a track impossible to follow. They paw their faces in discomfort, and can work only when sideways to the wind.

It is difficult to decide whether the man or the dog is better adapted mentally to pulling, but it is certainly true that, while he is actually at work, sledge-hauling tends to inhibit a man's intellectual ability almost completely. Dogs, from puppyhood, have been trained to pull, and to do this they are intensely eager, so long as their spirits are high. Men are never intensely eager to pull, and while hauling they develop a conscious dislike for the task. Tiredness and hunger will dispirit men and dogs alike, but there are other and totally different causes of this. Lack of comfort at night is very likely to lower the spirits of a team of men, and this was all too often the case in the 'pioneer' days of the Nansen cooker, when the night was spent in a damp and frigid semi-sleep. While the men, despite their tents and sleeping-bags, were wretched, the dogs could curl up, snug and happy in their long hair. The dogs remain as gay as ever, but the men may be discouraged. Dogs may be dispirited in quite another way, even when the men are the most eager and excited. The party may be travelling down a broad ice-filled channel with steep mountains rising up on either hand. The men are elated, for each day they see more than eye has ever seen before, new, towering ranges, great glaciers and icefalls. Of these, the dogs see almost nothing, and what is there of interest in a distant mountain, a far-off dark mass, except in the conscious consideration of it? The eyes of a dog are barely a foot from the ground, and slight undulations of the surface, unnoticed by the men, cut off their view completely. So to the dogs that journey, of greatest interest to the men, may be an everlasting drag over a weary waste of whiteness devoid of all exciting sights and smells. But a floe-locked iceberg, a sudden hummock of morainic stone, these are of the greatest interest and excite the dogs, though the men may pass with a simple glance. In the last stages of exhaustion the mind of man is his greatest source of strength, and it can force his weary starving body onwards far more powerfully than a whip can urge a dog that is hungry and physically worn out.

Apart from mental qualifications there are two occasions on which a team of men have the superiority in hauling sledges. All the men may leave the sledges to visit a point of special

U.S.S. GLACIER

(Official United States Navy photograph)

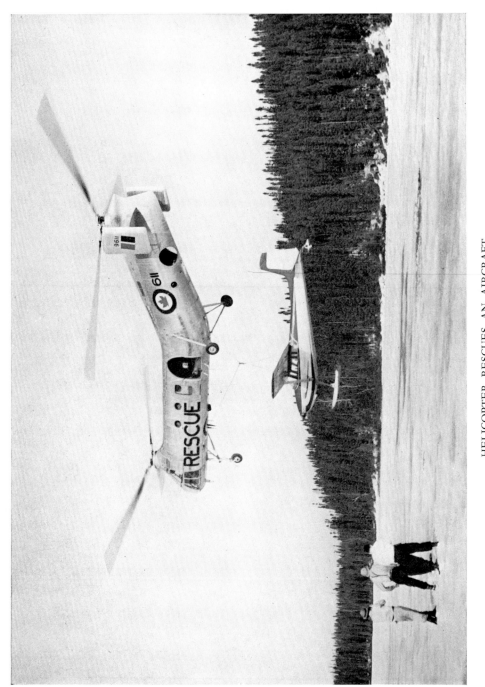

HELICOPTER RESCUES AN AIRCRAFT

interest at some little distance from the track. Though well-trained teams of dogs may be left to themselves for several hours, it is always wise to leave a man on watch. When much crevassed country is to be traversed, men are again superior in most instances, but a sufficiently well-trained team of dogs may excel even here.

So from the point of view of pure traction, dogs are more efficient than men. There is a further point in confirmation of this superiority. In a man-hauling expedition all the tractive power must be brought from home and fed from the beginning. There can be no change, neither increase nor decrease in its number. With dogs a generation is only a year or eighteen months. The pups will work at nine months old, and their number may be quickly increased. A generation in men is thirty years, and it has been the normal custom in the past for polar expeditions to leave all womenfolk behind.

We may continue our historical retrospect a little further, for perhaps at times the pendulum had swung too far in favour of dogs for use in polar journeys. Efficient traction was not the alpha and omega of polar travel. To think it so was a confusion of means with ends. Traction was not an end in itself, but the means only. The end, often, was the acquisition of information, and it was for this that efficient traction was needed.

Men possess the most efficient brains, and men are good but not the best traction animals. But men's brains will not work at their best when the bodies that house those brains are wearied with extreme exertion. On the other hand, dogs are the most efficient form of living traction, but unaided, they cannot obtain the information that is wanted. Now dogs and men must both be fed, whether they use their bodies, their brains, or both. If men sledge alone, dragging their loads without other help, bodies and brains are both available, and though the brains will not be at their best, there is but one set of mouths to fill. But if a journey depends entirely upon dogs for traction, the bodies and the brains are separate, and therefore two sets of mouths must be satisfied. The problem is to find what combination will lead to the gathering of the greatest amount of information in the particular circumstances. It may be that man-hauling will most advance this object; on the other hand, the use of dogs for all traction, the men acting as little more than brain-filled passengers, may be found more suitable. The choice should depend upon the circumstances, the kind of information that is sought, the time of year, the type of country, the numbers of men and dogs that can be used, and the time to be allowed for the journey. Other factors may also enter into account, but each occasion should be judged separately, treated as a separate problem and decided on its own merits. It may be that the use of dogs for all traction will most frequently lead to the best results, but it is a mistake to think that this always follows.

That was sound opinion in the later thirties, within a particular context of endeavour and before the advent of a convenient mechanical oversnow vehicle for general use in icecap travel.

Particularly in mountainous districts in the summer-time, simple man-hauling is still often likely to be more effective than dog transport. Imagine a lofty ice-bound coast that it is the intention to explore and map. The grand magnificence of the scenery dwarfs into insignificance the tiny eager men as they stare up at the mountains and glaciers, wondering what is beyond, and how best they can proceed. In places, the mountains dip so steeply to the sea that no ice can cling, and where less steep there are great cascading icefalls, quite impassable to man. The mountains stand as buttresses, their feet in the blueness of the water, their shoulders, razor-edged, among the clouds, joining them to the higher planes beyond. Between these gargantuan props run glaciers that bear away the overflow of inland ice, to end at last as leviathan bergs that plunge into the restless sea. From a distance the most likely route is known, and towards this the men drag their lightly-laden sledge. The weather is fine and warm for that country, the crevasses are widely open and visible, and runnels of water course at noon upon the glacier surface. The men are happy in the knowledge that they have a month before them and that, while summer lasts, they can travel light. The first crevasses are met and conquered, and the party mounts higher up the frozen stairs.

Another crevassed area is reached that seems to stretch completely across the glacier, and no obvious way is open. They halt and wait, trying with the glasses to unravel the maze, searching out a path that may wind across and back, this way and that way, until finally it emerges on the clearer slopes beyond. At last the path is seen and chosen, and then with slow deliberation they embark upon it. Great care at times is needed as they move along the thwartwise ridges, a yawning cavity on either hand, then sharply turn across a bridge of snow. The load is relayed in two halves so that the sledge is light and easily manoeuvred, and the risk of accident is lessened. The men know that they are safe so long as they tread with conscious care and do not force the pace, and after some hours' effort all is finally across, and they move upward towards their goal. In retrospect the men realise with complete certainty how much the better off they were this day without their dogs. Of course the strain upon the back and legs would have been much less, but the impetuous dogs would almost certainly have caused trouble. With all the dog food needed, the loads would have been much bigger, and so less manageable on the steep and slippery ridges. In fact, the risk would have been too great to allow them to come this way at all, for possibly some among the dogs, much needed at a later date, would have been lost in the yawning clefts, falling downward into the icy blue below.

This is but an example of an occasion when experience would suggest that men, not dogs, as drawers of the sledge, would bring the better results. Recent 'modern' examples of this special efficient use of man-hauling are to be found in a variety of small mainly geological ventures in Spitsbergen, and in the South Georgia Survey of the earlier nineteen-fifties. But even there, agreeing that sledge dogs were less useful and would have been out of place, some may fairly ask if, had it been possible on grounds of cost and availability, would not the men have been more efficient still had each man had the charge of two accompanying pack dogs, each with a load of 30 lb.? The answer probably is Yes.

This is the context into which the helicopter with easy confidence, and considerable cost, now flies. If not too far removed from its still excessive dependence upon specialised base facilities, the helicopter can render magnificent service in difficult mountain country otherwise only to be reached by the legs of man.

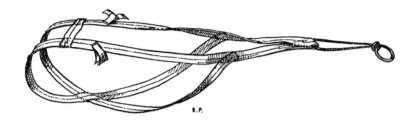

CHAPTER V

Transport

THE term transport normally covers both the actual source of locomotion, the power unit, and the object or vehicle which bears the burden from place to place and is moved by that power unit. In such an instance as the pack horse these two are merged in one, but more usually they are truly separable, the cart and the horse, or the engine and the train. Being separable, these two may be considered one at a time in their various uses and prospects with regard to polar life and travel.

Sources of locomotion available are muscular, environmental and mechanical, and the three have evolved in this order in time. Animals at first depended solely on their own efforts to move about their world, whether it was land or sea, an ocean or a single drop of water. But at a very early stage the trick was acquired by a number of organisms of allowing themselves to be carried passively by wind and water. Man himself, in his geologically brief history, has passed through the same stages, but has gone one further, so surpassing all his brother beasts. In his racial infancy man no doubt moved among the branches,

59

dependent upon his grasping hands, then walked and ran upon his feet.   Soon, gaining confidence, he punted or paddled his crude raft across the waters of shallow lakes or rivers.   Then, with mounting ambition, allowed himself to drift at ease upon the river's current and erected a sail to help him homeward from the sea.   His mind growing in initiative, invented the roller, then the wheel, then by gradual degrees and centuries of effort, at last the mechanical engine in its many forms and diverse uses.   The engine is simply a means of producing power by combustion of organic substances in an external contrivance instead of inside the contractile cells of man's own tissues. But even in this age of machines, probably the greatest source of locomotive power in the world is still in the aggregate this voluntary contraction of man's innumerable muscle cells.

All the different methods of self-propulsion found in animals, from the lowest to the highest, depend basically upon contractile tissues or substances.   Man, in making his machines, though producing the energy by external combustion instead of internally, has adopted several of these same methods.   For example, the violent projection of a jet of water, whereby squids dart with great rapidity, has been copied in principle in the projection of rockets, and in the swift evolution of jet aircraft engines in the last two decades.

Of all the conceivable forms of traction, three only have been found of use in polar transport on land, these being wind, legs and engines.   Beyond being a useful source of power at one place, the wind, through the medium of sails, has been used to a small extent as opportunity offered as a propulsive force, but its incidence and direction are altogether too unreliable for general use.   As for legs, whether they belonged to men, dogs or other quadrupeds, they proved the only really efficient mode of polar land locomotion up to the end of the first quarter of the present century, and much longer in many regions.   That dogs will long continue to render special polar services will ardently be hoped by all who have had that great satisfaction, the day by day working of a happy team.

A matter of particular importance is the simplicity of polar transport by dogs.   Though great experience is required to get the very best out of a team of dogs, a moderately high standard of performance can be quickly gained by men previously quite untrained in the art. Then, if one dog dies, is lost down a crevasse, or falls ill, only a fraction of the tractive power is lost. This is a great advantage over the internal-combustion engine, where much experience is required to deal effectively with all the minor defects to which an engine is liable, and these difficulties are made the greater by the coldness of the climate. Once a serious defect occurs, the complete machine is unusable, not simply a small portion of its power. On a uniform surface the speed of a tractor will far exceed that of a team of dogs. And the total loads which can be hauled by tractors are so great that dog power in truth cannot continue to compete in many operations. A further great advantage of any form of engine compared with dogs is that the living must be supplied with food at all times, whether they are working or not. The 'dead' tractor, on the other hand, consumes its fuel only when doing useful work. Theoretically this is so, but in practice, more particularly in North America, it is common practice under cold conditions to keep diesel tractor engines running without cease for days on end, whether at work or at rest. Let it ever be remembered too that living animals can reproduce themselves.

These are comparative considerations that come from the dogs and machines themselves, not from the ground over which they may attempt to travel, and in practice these 'ground' factors are often the more important. Always, in sledge-hauling over ice and snow, starting the load from rest is the first difficulty. A tractor cannot exert a pull until it is actually in motion, but dogs can haul on their traces while the sledge is still at rest. In practice, both usually start the load by taking a short rush, or producing a jerk which breaks the starting friction. In this the advantage of the more flexible dog-power is great. Since a single tractor represents much more power than a single team of dogs, the sledge load that it drags is proportionately greater, and so makes the starting friction still more difficult to overcome. Whenever either sea ice or bridged crevasses must be crossed, the great weight involved in a single tractor unit of any type will always be a serious drawback.

Experience has shown that where surfaces are known to be mainly uniform, smooth and flat, and where sea ice and large crevasses will not be encountered, a suitable tractor will be more efficient than dogs.   Where there is no such uniformity and the route includes sea ice and crevasses,* hills and steep descents, hummocks and leads, then dogs regain their supremacy.

Such remarks however now have an old world ring about them. So much depends upon material resources available. With the great recent development of polar exploration and exploitation, dog transport has already become as it were the bicycle on the side track alongside the trunk road roaring with heavy trucks and lorries. The poor, the old-fashioned, the sportsmen, those travelling in special conditions such as broken sea ice, will still cherish their dogs and swear by them, but the main stream is now that of the noisy, evil-smelling mechanical monsters which destroy the peace of the polar world.

It is now about 45 years since the first beginnings of effort to develop a motor sledge. Scott was among the pioneers. The inter-war years saw the invasion of the North American Arctic by caterpillar diesel tractors of standard design but modified for cold climate use. This trend has continued so that tractor trains and wannegans are now familiar on particular routes. The tractor hauls a set, commonly of three, heavily laden cargo sledges of which one, the wannegan, is the Arctic equivalent of the caravan. The tractor train cannot negotiate much broken ground nor particularly deep soft snow, but great loads can be hauled across the barren lands and along the natural routes provided by frozen lakes and rivers.

The second World War was the foster mother of oversnow vehicles, the most widely known of which, the 'weasel,' was not particularly designed for polar conditions at all. It was to be a general purpose small amphibious tracked vehicle. But soon it was discovered how admirably it could extend its amphibious prowess to oversnow travel and the hauling of cargo sledges. For the first decade after 1945 the 'weasel' became the maid of

* A recent innovation is an American system of crevasse detection electronically, which may greatly help mechanical vehicles in difficult country.

all work in Canada, Greenland, Antarctica and elsewhere. As a military vehicle, of United States design and manufacture, it became obsolete at the end of the War. But stocks have been sufficient for almost world-wide use. Only now is the public becoming aware of names, like 'Sno-cat,' which are the pioneer vehicles of the next stage, and which have been especially designed for oversnow use. Some, in this mechanical age, may perhaps claim to have become almost as reliant upon and affectionate towards their 'weasels' as their fathers and elder brothers towards their dogs. 'Weasels' have even been dropped by parachute from aircraft for Arctic exploration, and now in November 1956, at the South Pole itself.

Implicit in this discussion has been the assumption that the motive unit in polar transport must be designed to meet the polar topography, more particularly snow surfaces often of varying strength and driven by wind into the rough patterns of skavler or sastrugi. But now the minds of some, who have the material resources at their command, have turned towards the alternative approach. If, for example, transport across an ice sheet is essential and is to be regular, then modify the ice surface and use standard wheeled vehicles, rather than fit the vehicles to the ice sheet. North Greenland has already seen the beginnings of such techniques.

Turning now to aircraft in polar exploration, research and development, progress has been so rapid that it is worth quoting what seemed sensible in British eyes 20 years ago in the 'transitional' phase of polar work. By that means the extent of the change can be the more readily realised. But even 20 years ago we more conservative British were not fully profiting from the technical advances already available and in use elsewhere.

> In discussions of transport and exploration in polar lands the aeroplane can no longer be neglected. Moving at great speed and in comfort through an almost completely uniform medium, enormous stretches of country can be seen and photographed on clear days. If a safe landing can be effected a depot may be laid, or a mobile unit landed to carry out detailed observations that are impossible from the air. Landing and taking-off may be a difficulty unless there is available a permanent area of land or shelf ice. Otherwise there may be long periods when either drifting ice makes the use of floats impossible, or hummocks or thaw pools make skis equally impracticable as means for landing.

The weather may often make flying impossible, but the results of one successful flight may outweigh many disappointments. Photographs of the greatest value may be taken from the air, and maps constructed from them if enough control can be obtained from ground parties or by making landings at suitable points. In this way huge areas may be accurately surveyed that would take months of effort on the ground. Detailed geological and glaciological research, and many other forms of study, are, of course, impossible from the air. The great advantages of flight reside in the possibility of speedy reconnaissance and photographic survey, and in the rapid laying of small depots at distant points. Experience has shown, however, that the greatest care and caution are required in the interpretation of what is seen on a pioneer flight into new country if very serious errors are to be avoided.

The value of the aeroplane in polar exploration is accompanied by some serious disabilities. Aeroplanes, like tractors, require highly skilled attention, both in the actual flying and in ground service. To some degree these requirements may be met, but on an expedition the man who 'knows more and more about less and less' is to be avoided, and it is little use for a highly skilled aeroplane mechanic to fly over unknown country if he is unable to appreciate and interpret correctly what he sees. The greatest drawback of aeroplanes is their expense, both initially and in running costs, and in the amount of work and number of men required to keep them serviceable. This applies with no great force to a small aeroplane taken purely for purposes of short-range reconnaissance and local photographic survey. If, however, the machine be larger, it may become such a serious item of expenditure that it can no longer justify itself.

That was the United Kingdom small expedition point of view in the later thirties, and assuming that the aircraft must be maintained and serviced under primitive conditions and solely within a small expedition's own resources. At that date aircraft had already flown over both poles, the Arctic basin had been traversed, the Russians had begun to develop their skill in landing aircraft on the floes of the Arctic ocean, and much survey by aerial photography had begun in Canada (always a pioneer in Arctic techniques), in Greenland, Svalbard and elsewhere.

As in many other instances, it was war which stimulated polar flying and produced the machines that were fully capable. World War II caused much flying on reconnaissance into polar areas and, for example, the development of air facilities in Greenland as staging posts in the trans-Atlantic ferry service. The capabilities of aircraft in polar use have continued to extend enormously. Given the resources of men and material almost anything is possible. Size and speed have increased greatly. Landing can be on wheels, skis, floats or combinations of two of these. Visits of aircraft to the poles are no longer rare. United States planes have for a decade flown twice weekly on meteorological sorties from Alaska to the North Pole, and the Russians have followed rather similar pursuits, and the dependence upon aircraft in the Canadian north is truly remarkable. Civil airlines, with a Scandinavian pioneer, regularly now use a high latitude route. Navigation, in particular the use of the Greenwich grid instead of the normal lines of latitude and longitude beyond 70° N., has much advanced. And in early 1956 came the first long crossings of the Southern Ocean, by American aircraft from New Zealand to McMurdo Sound. Though not the first attempters, American flying over Antarctica has been predominant over that of all other nations, though still, let it be said, with some inevitable inadequacy of ground control which lowers the value of all photographic interpretation and subsequent map production.

The age of polar flying is not only now well under way, but the aerial transport of stores for use at isolated stations is commonplace as well. The obsolescent flying boat, in Canadian, Danish and British hands, has had notable successes in such operations; and many hope that even yet this type of aircraft will emulate the phoenix. Russian, wheeled aircraft likewise are notably efficient in landing upon and victualling floating meteorological stations on the north polar pack ice. Additionally there have been great developments in the dropping of supplies from the air, a swift procedure which avoids the needs and risks of landing. Drops on to snow surfaces are now commonly made from low altitudes without the use of parachutes, even oil drums suffering no more than small fractional losses. Parachutes can take anything, a delicate instrument, a man, or an over-snow vehicle. A climax has now come with the American establishment, by air, of an International Geophysical Year meteorological and other research station at the South Pole itself. From the first internal combustion engine to this transportational feat is still within the life span of one man.

Following on this discussion of different forms of motive power we may pass on to some consideration of sledges. As used in different parts of the world sledges vary greatly in construction, but all are devised on the principle of requiring the least possible effort to drag them. The differences of construction resulted from local conditions, physical and material. But as in so much else, original local differences are now disappearing. The surfaces to be traversed vary enormously from deep soft snow to hummocked and pinnacled pressure ice. The loads to be carried may be widely different, anything from a single hunter and his gear, to loads of several tons. For some native peoples wood was the available material, for others there was iron, and for some nothing but bone. All these factors have been reflected in the local type of sledge. Ingenious people in the Canadian archipelago have made strong and serviceable sledges of strips of Musk Ox skin, or even fish, placed and supported in position when supple, then soaked with water and frozen hard. Such sledges, being edible, had certain disadvantages. Sir John Ross, writing of his *Arctic Expedition*, 1829-33, mentions a case when "mutiny and rebellion broke out among the dogs. They had rid themselves of their traces and got loose; while, never being overfed, and at that time, doubtless, tolerably hungry, they had attacked the sledge of Awack for the purpose of devouring the frozen fish of which it was constructed, unless, indeed, they preferred the hides of the musk ox by which these were bound together."

Apart from the flat-bottomed toboggan type, including the Scandinavian pulk, for use where deep soft snow is general, sledges normally have two parallel runners, the width of runner and the material determined by the supplies at hand or the local conditions. The width of the runners, which provide the bearing surface of the sledge, must be great enough to resist the tendency to sink into the surface and so increase the labour of hauling. At the same time the runners must be strong and durable. The fact that a certain type of sledge is or has been used in a particular place, or by a particular people, does not necessarily mean that the type is best for use elsewhere, or best even in its own locality. Much depends on local conditions of snow and ice, temperature and topography, and for each area there must in theory be a sledge construction best adapted to it. The people living in an area have been so often limited in their constructive genius by the inadequacy of materials at hand, that the most efficient local sledge may never have been evolved. This was very true of certain of the Eskimo met by Sir John Ross's expedition, for "their sledges were singularly rude; the sides consisting of pieces of horn tied round and enclosed by a skin, and the cross bars on the top being made of the fore legs of a deer. One of them was but two feet long and fourteen inches wide, the others were between three and four feet in length. On the under part of the runner there was a coating of ice attached to the skin, rendering their motion very easy." This lack of quality in the local product may be found in every branch of equipment for life in polar regions. But the days when such comparisons were truly relevant are now in general passed.

Apart, again, from the toboggan type used in deep soft snow, most of the different forms of sledge to be found in northern lands fall roughly into one or other of two types. Either they may have broad runners of wood some 4 inches or so across, or the runners may be much narrower, when they are usually shod with strips of bone or iron. To meet the varying strains when travelling over uneven ground, a sledge of either type is of somewhat flexible construction, and the joints are simply bound with thongs instead of being more rigidly fastened. Typically, the sledge with narrow runners is used by coastal people to travel over sea ice and rough ground generally, while the broad runner is made of greater length and is used for smoother travel inland. The complete separation of the two types is the result of European influence, and is not so marked in the sledges of native races.

But such considerations of sledge design are fast becoming almost of archaeological interest, except to those happy mortals who can still rely upon their dogs for transport. Today, with more and more powerful mechanical haulage available, and far greater loads to be dragged, sledge design is a matter for the engineer. Great strength and rigidity have now almost

supplanted the earlier flexibility which was advantageous so long
as strength, rigidity and lightness were unobtainable together.

The actual resistance to a sledge's forward movement is two-
fold, the friction between the bearing surface and the snow or
ice beneath, and the resistance due to the sledge sinking into the
surface, and so piling up the snow in front of its various parts.
Efforts are made to keep both of these factors at a minimum.
Friction may be kept small by maintaining the smoothness of
the runners, clearing them of accumulations of ice or other
matter, or in certain circumstances covering their surface with a
smooth coat of ice or mud, or with thin sheets of metal.   The
friction between the runner and a snow or ice surface may vary
greatly.   As a general rule the colder the surface the greater the
friction, but this effect does not become important except at
very low temperatures.   When the temperature rises towards
the freezing point of snow the surface again becomes sticky,
more glue-like than gritty as it is when very cold.   Later a
névé surface may be produced, and on this the friction is extremely small.   The friction on an ice surface, whether it be
exposed hard and blue, or is merely a crust, will be always less
than on a snow surface, though a really hard wind-crusted surface
may differ very little from pure ice in this respect.   A further
factor, that increases the resistance between runner and surface,
is salt in the uppermost layers of the sea ice early in the year,
before there has been any thick blanketing with snow.   On
such a salty surface the friction may sometimes become so great
as to make it almost impossible to move a heavily-laden sledge.
The force required to start a heavy load is always great, often
enormous compared with the effort required to keep it moving.
The whole of the preliminary resistance is aptly summed up in
the engineer's colloquial term 'stiction.'   With heavily-laden
sledges the breaking of this 'stiction' is often a serious problem,
whether the form of traction is living or mechanical.

The greatest recent advances in sledge design have been
concerned with new friction-reducing surfaces for the runners.
Particular advantage has been found in certain bonded resin
surfaces and now more recently still in a curious material called
polytetrafluorethylene which, though still under trial, seems to

have remarkable potentialities, some of which have already been successfully demonstrated. One can but wish that such advances had been made early in the era before mechanical power became available, when the leg muscles of men and dogs provided all the effort. But still for decades yet dogs are likely to be used in special circumstances, among which are the police patrols in the administration and care of Canada's Eskimo population amid her Arctic archipelago, fur trappers in east Greenland and Canada, administrators and research workers in the sea-girt mountainous Falkland Islands Dependencies, and the great annual dog race in Alaska. There is thus still time for the low friction surfaces to play a valuable part in improved sledges, and of course in skis too. The importance of the new surface materials in the design of heavy mechanically-hauled sledges, is yet too early to judge.

The resistance to forward motion over and above the true friction, that due to the piling up of snow in front, is primarily dealt with by the forward curve of the runners, and by arranging the runners of such a width that the sledge will be borne up and allowed to slide upon the surface itself. Since, however, both the load and the surface are so extremely variable, and the wider the runners the more liable are they to injury, it is not feasible to do more than arrange the width of the runners as the compromise best suited to the local conditions. This matter of sinking into soft snow or breaking through thin ice is important. At the same time as the sledge takes a greater pull to move it, the power unit whether mechanical or living may likewise be in difficulties. These circumstances may be partly overcome by devices such as skis or snow-shoes, though these are of use to men alone, not dogs, while modern over-snow vehicles can have unexpectedly wide tracks. On thin sea ice it is probably the general sagging effect due to the load as a whole that determines whether or not the ice will break, rather than the actual loading measured as pounds per square inch. Again, the pressure exerted by the feet of dogs is greater than that of the feet of men, yet actually, in practice, men will generally break through first. This is because in walking a man carries his whole weight on each of his two feet alternately, and makes impact with the surface, while in slow going the dog has always on the ground more than half of its available support, and places its feet more gently down. Some figures for comparative loading are of interest.

TABLE SHOWING APPROXIMATE AVERAGE LOADING OF THE BEARING SURFACE OF A NUMBER OF ANIMALS AND OBJECTS.

	lb. per sq. in.
Pig	80
Motor car	40
Pony	15
Dog	$3\frac{1}{2}$
Narrow-runner sledge	3
	(with 1,000-lb. load)
Man	$2\frac{1}{4}$
Weasel	2
Broad-runner sledge	$1\frac{1}{4}$
	(with 1,000-lb. load)
Snocat	1
Man on skis	$\frac{1}{2}$

No consideration of polar transport today can be regarded as adequate without some discussion of polar ships. This is a large topic and here brevity is needed.

In the days of sail, beyond indeed the middle of the nineteenth century, almost any well-built wooden ship in good condition was fit for despatch for Arctic service. Some were obviously more suited than others but certainly there was no dearth of vessels, either naval or commercial, for work in ice. These old time, slow wooden vessels had a resilience and a hull form which produced a safety and a flexibility in use which has now sadly disappeared. Slow wooden ships can take the bottom, be squeezed, even lifted by ice, can be hauled ashore, even (and this has been done) deliberately sunk to the bottom to avoid the ice and recovered later intact. Nansen's *Fram* was the final peak in this evolutionary family. Scandinavia and Newfoundland remain now as the only owners of numerous small wooden vessels fit for northern pack ice.

The advent of propellers and power, speed and steel, have spoilt the ordinary ship for polar use. We are more limited

BLUIE WEST ONE AIRPORT, WEST GREENLAND

(*Photograph U.S. Army Air Forces, 1947*)

OPERATION DEEPFREEZE "LITTLE AMERICA FIVE"

(Official U.S. Naval Photograph

OPERATION DEEPFREEZE "TRAIL PARTY"

today than were our grandfathers in our movement in the polar regions in the normal ships of our time. Normal ships today must be treated with a great caution. Steel plates are easily ripped by ice when met at speed; standard hull construction cannot resist pinching between floes; and propellers are especially vulnerable. Naval vessels in general are even less suitable than merchant ships. Areas of light ice may be traversed by standard freighters on their own, but if heavier ice may be encountered then freighters must be convoyed by icebreakers. That is the normal practice along the Russian Northern Sea Route, in the victualling of the Canadian and American Arctic bases and stations from both east and west, and in such operations as the United States ventures into the Ross Sea. The Baltic has special comparable arrangements.

Apart from convoy work, vessels for the ice today must be constructed for their particular task, or be specially strengthened later to that end. There are many gradations between small 'sealers' and the largest 'icebreakers' but no standard classification. But it may well be asserted that no ship should be termed an icebreaker unless of over 4,000 tons—and some are over 10,000 tons*—and a ratio of horse power to normal displacement exceeding one. These vessels have remarkable features in great strength, high horse power, rocking tanks, and so on, which all combine to give a freedom of manoeuvre in ice which is truly wonderful. Apart from Baltic use, icebreakers today are owned in quantity only by the United States and Russia, while Canada has a small number, and Argentina one. The rest of the British Commonwealth and the rest of the world have none.

* A Russian atomic-powered icebreaker of 16,000 tons is about to be built.

F

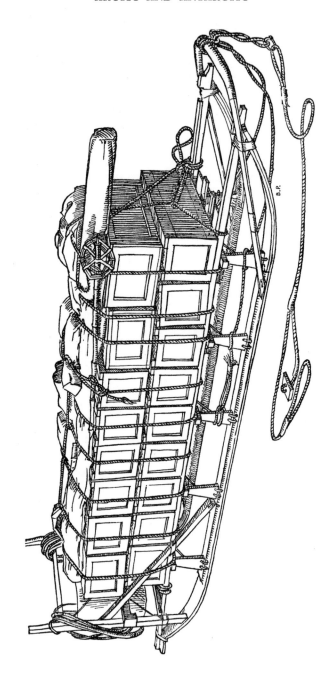

CHAPTER VI

Food

"Have no desires and you will be the richest man in the world."
—(Cervantes.)

FOOD on polar expeditions has long provided an interest to observer and participant alike. And more especially has there been interest in polar rations, the precise daily amounts and kinds of food to be eaten on long journeys where the difficulties of transport have necessitated curtailment to the absolute minimum to sustain life and a meagre efficiency. With the advent of mechanical transport in the 'modern' phase of polar exploration, this requirement has, in large measure, lost its urgency. But the topic remains of interest.

National food habits, the evolution of preservative methods and of packaging, cost, availability and other factors, all play a part in the history of polar provisioning. National food habits are most in evidence in ships and at shore establishments of a more or less permanent kind, and the differences from normality are not necessarily very great. More similar to each other are the rations for exploratory journeys at any particular date. None the less it needs to be stated that British food habits form the basis of this present consideration, and it is actual polar rations, the day to day travel diet, which is of greatest interest.

The polar travel ration is of course greatly influenced by the transport available, and it has been developed with greatest care for use when it is known that no supplementation from local resources is expectable. If the whole of the food needed for a group of travellers for several weeks or months has to be transported throughout, considerations of weight immediately become important. If, as has so often happened in the history of polar endeavour, the goal is the maximum journey, in distance and duration, then clearly the amount of food per man per day must be reduced to the absolute minimum consistent with survival. If animal transport is used the same basic consideration applies, except that on occasion, as loads diminish, so may the number of animals be reduced. The interconnection between rations, mode of transport, and the state of dietetic knowledge, must be very clear. The changes in this relationship may conveniently be traced briefly over those same stages in polar activity as we use elsewhere, namely before the first World War, between the wars, and since World War II.

In the 'pioneer' stage before 1914, detailed knowledge of nutritional principles was absent; vitamins were unknown as such; scurvy was an ever-present dread if not probability; and the legs of British seamen were the common transport for the longest of unsupplemented journeys. Against this background the swift skill of Amundsen's dog-drawn journey to the South Pole is all the more notable.

Between the wars, in the 'transitional' stage, transport by carnivores, dogs, was general; nutritional understanding was advanced; and the daily man ration, if not perfect, was quite adequate for long periods of happy efficient work without undue discomfort or hunger.

Since World War II, in the 'modern' phase, advances in nutritional knowledge have further improved the man ration, though only by a little; while at last dog rations have begun to receive the research which they had long deserved. But, in parallel, the rapid advance of over-snow vehicles and air support has much diminished the need and incentive for perfected rationing. A vehicle which must drag barrels of liquid fuel measured in tons, will not be overloaded because its driver's food weighs a few more ounces for each day's journey than is strictly necessary.

Indeed it must now be recognised that as dietary knowledge has allowed the perfecting of man and dog rations to their present peak of efficiency, so has their utility largely faded by the swing to mechanical transport and the improbability of attempting the maximum possible self-sufficient journey without it. Nevertheless a real usefulness remains which will, in particular areas, be exploited for some decades yet by men with dog sledges not yet over-passed by helicopters. So some further consideration here is needed, but proportionately less than when the first edition of this book appeared at the end of the interwar 'transitional' period.

Much thought, effort and ingenuity have gone into the development of polar rations in the course of the last fifty years, and indeed for a century earlier.* Insufficient knowledge of nutritional principles, lack of perspective and, more especially, lack of controlled experiment, have all had their successive influence on the evolution of polar rations.

Throughout the course of the deliberate development of polar rations certain assumptions and criteria have had special significance. The availability of ample water has always been assumed. Lightness of weight has been of extreme importance. High calorie content has been urgently sought as, in recent times, has nutritional completeness in terms of several months, and a suitable ratio of protein, carbohydrate and fat. Further features are simplicity in preparation, sufficient palatability, and permanence of quality in store. Subsidiary have been such

* Acknowledgment is made to the Nutrition Society from whose *Proceedings* certain paragraphs are here quoted. See contribution by the present author to a Symposium on "The Provisioning of Expeditions in the Field," on 26th October 1953. (*Proc. Nutr. Soc.*, 1954, **13**, 69-73.)

aspects as retention of quality during passage through the tropics, packaging against the teeth of dogs and the effects of extraneous water, and the limitation of expense. In fulfilment of these requirements, it is worthy of note that some of the very earliest canned foods to be made were used in polar travel. Particular mention may be made of the preserved meats, soups and vegetables which formed part of the stores taken by Sir Edward Parry on his Arctic expeditions between 1819 and 1825.

A polar ration is normally looked upon as being a standard-ised diet for use when travelling by sledge in regions of low temperature, where the environment can be relied upon to provide nothing more than an inexhaustible supply of frozen water, where great bodily exertion is normally to be expected, and where heat loss will be extremely high and varied. It is usually reasonable to assume a good initial bodily reserve of fat, built up, or to be replenished, at a base camp where ample food is available. The problem, in its simplest terms, is the provision for the traveller of a diet that is nutritively complete in the normal sense, yet possesses the maximum amount of calories in proportion to its total weight. The exclusion of water and indigestible matter, and an increase in the amount of fat, are obvious, important features. Indeed the fat content of the ration may be so high as to be distasteful or even nauseous during the first few days of a journey.

Requirements in terms of Calories have been judged by trial and error, by expediency in limiting total sledge loads, by subjective inference and so on, rather than by experiment or any sure knowledge. Hunger is by no means a safe measure of inadequacy. The maximum, even the average, energy require-ment of the polar traveller in differing conditions is still not satisfactorily agreed. It must obviously be extremely varied; some have put the figure as high as 6,000 Calories, or even more. Much lower figures were recently mentioned at the Physiological Conference at Montreal in 1953. For example, it is asserted that trappers in Greenland managed with 3,000 Calories daily, miners in Spitsbergen with 4,500, and that members of the U.S. armed forces, and Eskimos in tests in Alaska, consumed from 3,000 to 3,500. The effectiveness of bodily insulation is a most important factor, as is the extent of space heating for a part of the 24 hours. The usual rations of British non-mechanised polar expeditions in the last 20 years have provided rather over 4,000 Calories a day in a net weight for the ration of about 30 oz.

The matter that obtrudes itself into these considerations, though as yet insufficiently recognised, is the innate variability in the physiological efficiency of individuals who may, in addition, differ considerably in size. There is no doubt that the dairy and pig farmers know much more of good and bad doers, and individual variations in that field, than is known to the human physiologist, who all too often clings to an erroneous belief in the equality of man. There are, however, strong reasons connected with psychology and morale against differentiating between individuals in the rations they may consume on an arduous sledge journey. What has in fact happened is that in polar travel a very real hunger has been normal, but the extent of the true deficit from man to man has gone unmeasured.

The literature of polar travel provides interesting examples of men suffering from food dreams. All those that I have come upon, in their insistence on carbohydrates and fats, are presumably a clear sign of calorie shortage. The extent to which man's body can usefully force to the conscious attention of his brain precisely what is lacking in his diet is a topic of great interest. Detailed experiment seems lacking, though perhaps much more is known about it than I am aware.

The mental processes accompanying stages of increasing hunger are peculiar. At first there are the simple feelings of the hungry little boy; then comes a hunger that is ever-present, but not always in the consciousness. Gradually the consciousness of hunger grows until it is always uppermost in the mind, and talk of food becomes the normal conversation. The body seems to suggest to the mind what it most requires. A good example of the usual craving for fat is quoted by Shackleton. When returning from the furthest south and rapidly approaching starvation, the talk was much of food:

"The 'Wild' roll was admitted to be the high water-mark of gastronomic luxury. Wild proposed that the cook should take a supply of well-seasoned mince meat, wrap it in rashers of fat bacon, and place around the whole an outer covering of rich pastry, so that it would take the form of a big sausage roll. Then this roll would be fried with plenty of fat."—(*The Heart of the Antarctic.*)

The consciousness of hunger increases until it is a pain that gnaws inside ceaselessly, except for the few minutes immediately after the scanty meals. Quite early the desire for food becomes insistent in sleep at night as well as waking by day. A peculiar form of sensation, food dreams, become a regular occurrence. In these the hungry mortal imagines food set before him in profusion, the tables laden with good things of every kind. Yet in these nightly dreams, some accident, some impediment or horrible embarrassment, occurs each time to thwart the hungry soul craving for his nourishment. In sleep, the man who has laboured through the day in biting cold and wind, only rewarded in the evening by a few ounces of pemmican and biscuit, sits down an honoured guest at a great banquet. Lord mayors in chains of office, high dignitaries of church and state, officers in Her Majesty's forces, resplendent in uniforms and robes, sit at the long tables, while scores of waiters bring forward great dishes of roast pork, bacon and suet puddings, all of them bubbling in thick fat and sending out the most enchanting odours. The honoured guest receives his portion, his lips water as he raises the first succulent lump to his mouth; he casts down his eyes, he stares with horror and rushes headlong from the hall, the feast untouched—his clothes have vanished.

Such are the food dreams of healthy and happy, albeit hungry men: awful must be the dreams of persecuted men, confined and starved in prisons.

Even when the hungry traveller at last reaches the lands of plenty, unless he has almost superhuman self-control, still further pains await him. When for the first time his stomach is nearly full, the desire for more is by no means satisfied. He eats more, and more again, and then come the most frightful feelings of inward oppression, and the intestines, stimulated by unwonted plenty, writhe with painful violence. But in spite of this new pain the returned traveller is happy, for he knows his work is done, and he only has to wait a little and then the pains will cease, and he can eat again without thought for the morrow.

Precisely upon what, then, has this hungry traveller been attempting to sustain himself upon his journey over the hundreds of miles of ice and snow? In the modern sledging ration the kinds of foodstuff are very limited in number, and their preparation is quick and simple, both most important points. For convenience the members of a party must take the major portion of their rations at the same time and in the same way, but each man can display his private likes in a multitude of minor variations. Breakfast consists of a plate of porridge made from quick-cooking oats, which have the advantage that if put into the pot when cold, the porridge is made by the time the ice has come to the boil. On top of each man's portion is placed an equal lump of margarine or butter, which melts into a tasty yellow oil. When sledging, it is essential for happiness to have the sugar ration in the form of lumps, and then the individual can decide exactly how he will distribute his share throughout the day. At breakfast too, some like to eat a small part of their day's biscuit supply. Lunch, taken at a brief halt in the middle of the day, is carried by each man separately, in a little cotton bag. In it he has, according to his private method of eating his allowance for the day, a portion of biscuit, a piece each of margarine and pemmican,* and perhaps a few lumps of sugar. With his companion he shares a thermos of cocoa, which is taken at every meal. Supper is the main meal of the day. Then each man has a plate of hot pemmican thickened with pea flour, and enriched with floating lumps of margarine. Some people, both for breakfast and for supper, prefer a mixture of porridge and pemmican. Following this there may be a piece of biscuit with a little more margarine, and then the precious chocolate, consumed as slowly as possible to prolong the pleasure. Chocolate, when very cold and hard, has much less flavour, and can be improved by singeing in the Primus flame, the burnt and softened edges being licked off little by

* Pemmican is a highly concentrated meat food, consisting of dried lean beef and pure fat, and is carried in sealed tins. The pemmican used by recent British expeditions has been of two kinds, that for men consisting of 45 per cent. protein and 43 per cent. fat, while dog pemmican contains 65 per cent. protein and 28 per cent. fat. These are rough figures.

little. Such is the total of the day's food, and it is very quickly gone. Almost the whole diet consists of slops: beyond the small amount of biscuit there is little to chew, a common complaint against invalid diet. This is the standard sledging ration, and this is the food calculated to supply just as much energy to the body as it is forced to expend. But often the ration must be reduced, so that the body must call upon its own reserves: and it is of course for precisely such occasions that the body has laid down those stores of fat which in civilised life are both so commonly deplored and so easily acquired.

In a polar climate, the loss of heat from a warm-blooded animal's body is very great. No reliable figures are available, but, in the course of cold-weather sledging, it is probable that often more than half the total energy content of the food is used simply to maintain the body's temperature. This is a most important point, applying equally to men and dogs, for it means that in planning the size of the ration, the severity of the cold that will be experienced is at least as important as the amount of the expected physical work.

The following table gives the amount and composition of a modern daily ration, for a man on an extended polar journey, the eating of which has just been described.

AMOUNT OF DAILY RATION, OBTAINED BY AVERAGING THE FIGURES FOR
SEVERAL RECENT BRITISH POLAR EXPEDITIONS, NORTH AND SOUTH

		ozs.	
Pemmican ..	.. ..	7	
Margarine ..	.. ..	6	
Biscuit ..	.. ..	3	Also small quantities
Pea flour ..	.. ..	2	of special vitamin
Oatmeal ..	.. ..	3	extracts.
Sugar ..	.. ..	$3\frac{1}{2}$	
Cocoa ..	.. ..	1	
Milk derivatives ..	..	$2\frac{1}{2}$	
Chocolate ..	.. ..	3	
		31 ozs.	

Such is the amount, a little less than two pounds, that the modern (if non-mechanised), polar traveller hopes that he will be able to have each day on a sledge journey away from all local supplies. Often circumstances will force him to diminish this ration, and a decrease to about 26 oz. per day for a good many weeks is no great discomfort if he starts out in good condition, with plenty of reserves in his body. Although the full ration seems able to provide the energy that the body needs to prevent real physiological deficiency, it by no means prevents a general feeling of hunger. This is true also of the dogs, to whom the modern practice is to give one or one and a quarter pounds per day of pemmican. But in this 'modern' phase of polar activity, in large measure these paragraphs have been describing history rather than practice.

Without here embarking on further analysis into food constituents, it is clear that the proportions of protein and fat are very high. Indeed the traveller has deliberately become a practising carnivore. Likewise, when man wants a beast of burden to help him in regions where food is scarce, or where the bulk of that food must be carried from the start of a journey and particularly in places of great cold, he must choose a carnivore. Of all the animals that man has domesticated there is one alone that is a carnivore by nature, the dog. Camels in northern China, ponies in Iceland and in Manchuria, yaks in Tibet, reindeer in northern Eurasia, sheep in the Himalayas with their little loads of borax, llamas in the high Andes, all are at work in regions of comparative cold. The difference between them and the dog is that all must travel slowly, daily seeking the scant vegetation that the rigorous climate allows, and unable on account of its bulk to carry with them food for more than a very few days. This is not to say that ponies, for example, cannot be used in polar work. Attempts, in some ways surprisingly successful, were made by Scott and Shackleton to use them in the Antarctic, and by others in the north, but clearly they were not as efficient as dogs would have been under the same conditions. The ponies might have been given a less vegetarian diet than was actually the case, but still the number of days' food that they could drag was bound to be far less with them than dogs. The elder Nordenskiöld used reindeer for pulling sledges over large and desolate tracts of country in

Spitsbergen. He found that they were excellent haulage animals, and pulled splendidly large loads of equipment and stores for his men. But it was necessary to feed them, for no supplies of that luxuriant lichen, reindeer moss, were obtainable by the way. More reindeer had then to be taken, pulling sledges laden with great bales of moss to feed those hauling the main baggage. So the vicious circle continued. The food of these herbivores is of such bulk that the distance which useful loads can be dragged is strictly limited. Ultimately, all the herbivores must starve together, but the carnivorous dogs may, *in extremis*, be induced to turn cannibal as required.

It is of interest to remember that, of all the herbivores turned partly carnivore to meet the harshness of the road, the camel is pre-eminent. At dusk, before the gates of Mukalla in southern Arabia, one may see a thousand camels couched each before its pile of dried sardines. When young the camel must be held by the nose and fed with leaves while an occasional fish is thrust into the corner of its mouth. But, when full grown, the fish are taken with avidity, in preparation for the long and foodless marches inland from the coast across the stony desert to the cities of the Hadramaut. Two stone of dried sardines is no unusual evening meal. So is the oil of the ocean's crustacean plankton, by the aid of the Indian oil sardine, converted into fat on the backs of camels, which will carry the imported cereals from the coast far inland to those strange many-storied mud-brick cities, whose main support is the subsidies sent by their sons trading in the East Indies.

Quite apart from the food that they can drag upon the sledge, the carnivores have other advantages in polar lands. Inland travel in Antarctica offers no chances of food by the way, but in the Arctic it is often possible. In both regions, coastal or sea ice travel is common, and along such routes seals are commonly to be found lying beside their breathing-holes or to be drawn up on a harpoon line. Then, when the adventurous herbalist creeps hungry into his tent, and his reindeer stamp their spreading feet and starve outside, close by the meat-eater gorges himself on brains and liver, while his dogs curl up replete. Even in Antarctica, many miles from the sea, single

seals have been found, thin, battle-scarred and dying, yet pro-
viding food for the carnivore.   Again, on the banks of a great
meandering river in northernmost Siberia an ivory tusk projects.
The warmth of spring sends down a mass of swirling waters;
the river eats back its walls; and there, at last exposed, lies the
rotting carcase of a mammoth after centuries of preservation by
permafrost.   On occasion even this has served for food, and
some have been thankful for it—incidentally including some who
attended a notable dinner of the Explorers' Club in New York.

Returning now again to the standard sledging ration, it
seems a fair assertion that in its evolution the factor of palatability has played no great part.   The healthy and willing human
organism, working at low altitudes, when hungry and having
no choice of diet, is well content with what is available.   Lack
of palatability has rarely obtruded except when there has been
choice.   This remark is however probably not true among the
explorers of high mountains.   There seems to be an altitude
effect, so that planners have to take a note of palatability and
personal preference which is redundant for normal polar work.

It is the author's strong suspicion that keeping a polar
expedition at all times on a humble but adequate diet will achieve
a greater contentment than its provisioning with a large assort-
ment so that choice must be exercised.   This statement refers
however solely to parties of educated and intelligent volunteers
ready to accept a severe personal discipline.   For military
rations under Arctic conditions—rations for cold weather warfare
—quite other considerations obtain, of which meeting innate
conservatism of food habits is one.   This belief, in a correlation
between humble adequacy and contentment, refers in particular
to people from the British Isles.   To those from North America
such thoughts will seem merely foolish and heretical: they may
none the less represent the truth.

Intelligent and isolated Britons, hardworking and hungry,
will happily build and sustain strength, vigour, purpose and
happiness on a steady diet of ample seal meat, bread, margarine,
sugar and jam, and very little else besides.   They will supple-
ment this basic diet with fish or penguin eggs—and they can
store birds eggs in flour for months—and they will retain a

small stock of special delicacies for occasional parties.   On this
diet, which in fact is both cheap and convenient, they can store
fat in their bodies for supplementing their specialised and much
more expensive sledging rations when they set out on their
exploratory journeys.   This is in fact a simple example of that
truism, which is so mistakenly and widely neglected, that, once
a quite low threshold has been surpassed, increased material
resources are by no means correlated with lasting contentment.
Contentment, when in isolation in a polar land, has many
connections with food, so that such considerations as these are
well worthy of more careful attention than they commonly
receive.

CHAPTER VII

Organisation and Leadership

THE organisation and leadership of polar expeditions are topics of perennial interest which change and evolve from generation to generation, even from decade to decade. Again the conception of stages is helpful to understanding the transition—and here one is dealing with generalities—between the older maritime expeditions, through the phase of private enterprise of the earlier decades of this century, to the larger efforts of today which once more are mainly managed as government ventures. The history of British polar endeavour provides, to him who likes to ponder, a convenient and lengthy series for purposes of comparison.

The 'pioneer' stage, before 1914, included all the earlier expeditions. They were, in general, marine ventures despatched by a national navy or by some far-sighted commercial company. Their marine nature resulted in their organisation being based on the normal customs of a ship or 'service', and the leadership was the apex of a normal pattern. A standard system of discipline, of rank, duty and command permeated the whole. From the leader to the most humble boy, all might be volunteers or be despatched, but all fell automatically within a consciously recognised familiar system: each man knew his place, and was indeed kept in it. Government, naval, or 'service' system had, and still has, great advantages. The chief of these is that the polar venture, however novel geographically or otherwise, is a continuation and extension of that which is normal and familiar, both in organisation and, in part, in equipment, and in the chain of command. The whole is professional in the best sense. The 'captain' or 'leader' in the field can concentrate upon leadership, upon the well-being of his people both physically and psychologically, and upon planning of both the strategic and the tactical order. He is helped by a competent staff which, again, is extending the familiar to the less familiar. But these 'pioneer' stage activities depended upon a particular climate of national policy such as existed in Britain for most of the nineteenth century. A comparable background of national policy exists again now in the United States today, which typifies the reversion in the 'modern' phase to the early pattern of great naval ventures.

National policy being furthered by the use of the 'service' machine—that is to say by a special use of one of a government's armed forces—has the immense advantage that is never allows an excessive range of responsibilities, duties and activities to come to rest on the shoulders of the leader, shoulders not always well prepared by experience or temperament to bear quite such diverse burdens.

The great British Antarctic ventures, of the first 15 years of the present century, typify the gradual transition from the older 'pioneer' stage to the 'transitional' stage, the inter-war period of private enterprise. Scott, for example, bore the great burden of money-getting for his ventures—though with the help of a few great patrons—and of many other problems which do not normally fall upon naval men. But he was able, in form if not in law, to carry forward the familiar naval pattern of organisation and command with all the advantages which thereby accrued. Some disadvantages there were, perhaps in some lack of flexibility, but on balance many of the 'service' advantages of the 'pioneer' stage were retained. The days of Franklyn were gone, the days when participation in a national polar commission was the outlet for vigour and the road to naval promotion. Scott, Charcot, Shackleton, Bruce and Amundsen, to mention but the most familiar, represent in their mode of leadership the beginning in the Antarctic of the change from what was typical of the 'pioneer' to the 'transitional' inter-war phase. But before the first World War many of the added burdens of 'transitional' stage organisation and leadership had not emerged.

The 1920s and 1930s made up the 'transitional' stage, the reign of private enterprise. National policies (apart from Russia) nowhere fully embraced polar endeavour. It was the period of vigorous amateur effort, motivated perhaps by little more than the love of high adventure enlivened by scientific

LOADING A WEASEL INTO A C-82 TRANSPORT AIRCRAFT

(Photograph by Maynard M. Miller)

A NEWLY-LANDED WEASEL BEING DRAGGED BY ITS
TWO 100-FT. PARACHUTES

(Photograph by J. Malcolm Greany)

TWIN-ENGINED "BEECHCRAFT," 18 R AIRCRAFT, ON AIR-STRIP
AT MAUDHEIM

SURVEY AIRCRAFT ON *NORSEL*, "NORSELBUKTA"

(Photographs by C. W. M. Swithinbank, "Norwegian–British–Swedish Antarctic Expedition, 1949-52")

curiosity. But the amateurs, as it were, kept the flag flying until the renewed reasons of national policy during and after World War II produced the present 'modern' phase. The pattern of 'modern' organisation and leadership has today come round full circle to a close approximation to the earlier 'pioneer' stage.

Before proceeding to describe the particular problems in organisation and leadership which today beset the 'amateur' leader where he survives in this 'modern' political world, it may be worth while re-reading paragraphs on leadership written in 1939 when, outside Russia, the 'transitional' stage seemed the normal, and the great 'modern' national, government, or 'service' ventures were yet unborn and unexpected.

The successful arrangement of all the necessities of life for a polar expedition, its provisioning with foodstuffs to last two, or even three years, the selection of travelling gear, and all the other innumerable items of equipment that stand between relative success and failure, is a task that requires experience and organising ability of a high order.   In some ways this task is more difficult than formerly, on account of the very specialised nature of certain parts of the equipment, for example, wireless and aeroplanes.   But, on the other hand, there is now vastly more experience to be gathered from the past, both in regard to the equipment itself and the procedure official, and unofficial, so easing the difficulties of the modern organiser to an extent that compensates at least for the newer difficulties.

The greater part of this book has been devoted to one aspect alone, the physical principles that underlie life and travel in the cold regions of the earth, together with the way in which these determine the equipment that is needed.   This is an intricate subject of its own that requires much thought and experience, but let it not be thought that even the most successful mastery of this aspect of an expedition will lead automatically to the success and efficiency of the whole venture.   The thing that counts far more than this physical equipment is the mental equipment of the party, and this does not mean just intellectual ability.   It is what may be termed the 'spirit' of the party that is all-important.   Exploits of men in the past shine for ever as examples of what may be done by a high spirit, real courage and initiative without the advantages of modern equipment.

The spirit of a party of differing people is like the courage of an individual, part is an in-born quality, and part is instilled and inspired by contact with others.   The in-born part of the expedition's spirit depends upon the several characters of the men that the leader chooses to accompany him, while much arises from the interplay of these characters one with another and with their leader.   Thus, the leader becomes the cardinal factor, and it is his ability and force of character that control the 'spirit' in the party, and very largely determine the results of the entire enterprise. It is he who chooses the men in the beginning, and it is he who moulds them once the party is gathered together.

Yet, though they understand the circumstances of an expedition to be peculiar, many people wonder why one member should be able to exert such an influence upon the others. 'Surely,' they will say, 'any member of the expedition with a vigorous personality will leave his mark upon the others.' They are quite right, but the mark left will be small compared with that left by the leader. In the little state that is an expedition, the form of government is of necessity an ultimate authority vested in the leader, albeit the authority may be a happy and benevolent autocracy. In all matters the leader's word is final; there is no appeal. The leader's decisions cover every phase of life, and not only sledging plans and rations. In any society half at least are as wax under the moulding hands of others in matters concerning their spirit, and their attitude towards life and their fellows. The leader will ever be as the master craftsman, fashioning as he will despite the efforts of the apprentices, and controlling those with a vigorous personality, even when they urge another way. It is unconscious influence that affects another man far more than any actual order given. So it comes about that it is the ordinary way of life of the leader that controls the general attitude of each man to his work and to his companions, and the amount of effort which the individual contributes to reach the goal of scientific discovery. Thus, the single factor that counts the highest in the attainment of the end is the personality and personal ability of the leader, his outlook on life, his motives and objects in leading the expedition, and the quality of the men that he chooses to follow him. The supreme importance of leadership is as great today as it has ever been. Where in the last century a second-rate leader could, if necessary, to some extent hide behind a mask of stern naval discipline, in these days of the more co-operative expedition, he must stand or fall on his own merits.

It is the duty of the leader to lead, and there is more in leadership than planning and directing and physically advancing in the forefront. By his every word and action a leader is leading his men, from day to day, even from moment to moment, moulding their behaviour one to the other, inspiring and directing their ardour for the work in hand, guiding them at all times in contentment or in depression. He sets the example in all things and at all times, not merely when he drives the leading team, choosing with experienced care the safest route across the young sea-ice, or a path up a crevassed glacier. The members of a polar expedition live in such intimate contact that, though some of his followers may be unconscious of it, the effect of the leader on the others is far greater than they may suppose. If the leader be cheerful his men will be cheerful; it the leader be hard-working and pertinacious in the face of adversity, so likewise will those under him become. The equipment and knowledge of the principles of polar life and travel are necessary, but it is the leadership and spirit instilled into the men that wins the day, be it in wresting knowledge from Nature or battlefields from the enemy.

But what is the real nature of this material that is said to be so plastic; what manner of men are the members of a polar expedition? The men are much as others—some big, some small, some dull, some clever. A certain standard of physical fitness is naturally required, but beyond that there are the normal variations in ability, humour, tolerance, religious outlook and desire to know. But in a confined life of close mental and physical contact the qualities that make up men's natures stand in different relationship to one another. At home, where escape is easy, it is fun to cross swords for a brief while with an intolerant creature filled with his own ability and self-righteousness. Then relief can come in another place in friendly talk with that member of an almost different species, a tolerant free-thinker filled with good humour, and ever ready to learn more. But on an expedition there can be no escape. So that, though to some degree everybody is infected, intolerance and lack of mental vitality would be serious drawbacks, both to the peace and good fellowship of the party, and to the quality of the work that is done. Apart from the specialised abilities (as those of the doctor, wireless operator or geologist), tolerance and eagerness to know and find out are the most valuable assets in an expedition member. But the tolerance required is vastly more than the absence of bigotry or prejudice, it must extend to all the little things of life, habits and talk no less than principles and opinions. Only in an atmosphere of tolerance can the eagerness to know flourish and bring the best results. For by its fruits the tree is judged, the expedition by the knowledge gained, though some may stress the thrills, thinking accidents and death of greater worth than real achievement. The degree of tolerance required to achieve the best results on a polar expedition is by no means easy to develop or to keep. At home the individual may believe himself a person of tolerance and good humour, little realising that the men with whom he spends the most part of his time are men of his own choosing. They get to know one another, and are friends simply because in many ways they are similar, hold views that tally, have similar interests and the same general outlook on life. People seldom understand the extent to which their environment of human contacts is of their own choosing, and naturally each chooses what he likes. But on an expedition, though the general physical environment is the individual's choice, the human environment is not. Not until personally involved in such a throwing together of individuals do many realise the extent of basal differences between people, even of the same social upbringing, and the extent to which in the past they have chosen companions similar to themselves. The extent of the mental conditioning produced by the individual's early surroundings, and the outcome of a different environment playing upon a different hereditary make-up, these are scarcely recognised except by the person who has consciously studied human nature. Until this recognition comes, the acquirement of true toleration is hardly possible. Two men may hold views that are totally opposed to one another on a subject, the 'right' view of which each considers essential to the living of a decent life. It is very difficult for both not to have a feeling of self-righteousness and pity for the other poor deluded person, and for both not constantly to try and show his error to the other. But for real peace and happiness over a long period of time, each must realise that the other may have as good reasons for his view, or if he has not, that pointing out his wrong at every opportunity will not help him to good temper. Good-humoured tolerance must be the aim throughout, but it must be a tolerance that is an understanding of a difference, not a condoning of inferior standards.

However much concealed his views and character normally may be, in the course of months together on a polar expedition, without the blurring of reality that is the normal social life at home, a man's companions will obtain, if they care to see, a true rendering of his qualities in a way that is very rarely possible at home. Virtues and vices are found where least expected, strength and weakness where unknown before. Over many months of living together in confined quarters, no dissimulation can so cloak a character that behaviour and reactions, discussion and teasing, will not lay it bare.

Even so, for those who have never experienced it there is still a difficulty in realising quite how constraining is the physical and mental contact in which these diverse people must live on an expedition. Those who have sailed in small ships will understand to some degree, but in these days the voyage is relatively so short that the end is never more than a few weeks or at most, months, away. But for the members of a polar expedition, for reasons of strength, transport and economy, their house is purposely made as small and simple as possible, and there they live together. When parties travel abroad into the surrounding empty land, again they must stick close together, and at night creep together into a tiny tent. For some, the closeness of this physical and mental contact, month after month, has no conscious drawbacks, but there are others more sensitive, for whom it may require the greatest efforts of self-control always to keep the peace. Let those who sleep in bedrooms, dine in dining-rooms and daily meet others of both sexes, try to feel what it would be like to live with less than a dozen others of the same sex, for many months on end, talking together, working together, sleeping always within six feet of another; and all this, by day and by night in the same room, with the same companions with the same conversations and stories, and the same efforts to pretend that the same jokes are entirely novel. In these circumstances the leader has the greatest opportunity to lead, to implant in others his own aspirations, to show by example how to work mentally and bodily to the full, and to keep a cheerful countenance when things go ill.

Those remarks from 1939 may now seem naïve in some degree but they were acceptable then as true and the truth in them remains. It is the whole perspective in polar exploration and research which has changed today alongside the tremendous changes in national policy and interest in things polar. Today the motivation of the great national efforts in the polar regions are political, strategic and scientific; then they were chiefly adventurous and scientific. Motivation and modes of action vary greatly from nation to nation: some are greatly influenced by past custom which is carried forward anachronistically into the changed world of today, while others, mostly those with great resources, look forward and more readily embrace that which is new. The younger nations and regimes are perhaps the more flexible and forward in polar endeavour today.

The private enterprise 'transitional' type of organisation and leadership, the hang-over from the past as our foreign competitors seem to say, is now scarcely to be found outside Great Britain, and France too, which has seen a remarkable recrudescence of polar activity in the last decade. Much that is good is lost in the present gradual extinction of private enterprise and we may regret its passing. But facts must be faced: in the world today the burdens upon the leadership in large private enterprise ventures are well nigh insupportable, and national policies may best be pursued by national activities in the polar regions as elsewhere. According to circumstances private activities may chance either to further or to embarrass nations and their policies: the history of the British Commonwealth, more particularly in Africa, provides ample instances of both.

The private leader of a great polar venture today must be a paragon. He needs to combine in his single over-burdened yet enthusiastic person not only the skills of the pioneer in the field, but the graces of the public speaker, the ingenuity and efficiency of the professional money collector, and as well be versed in a sufficiency of complicated sciences and techniques. All these attributes and others he must have in addition to those which are perhaps sufficient for the leader of a government 'service' enterprise, with its familiar pattern of support and backed by the national exchequer. All leaders must have courage, great perscipience, skill in the judgment of men, enthusiasm, self-confidence and that extra something which engenders trust and the wish to be led. They must, too, have a singleness of purpose if ever they are to achieve their goal in the difficult circumstances of today: it is for their friends to foster the leaven of full perspective.

Like bishops, upon whose mitred heads are heaped far too

great a multiplicity and variety of duties to be adequately
supported by any one man however nobly he strives, so with
the leaders of large private enterprise polar ventures in the
world today. We admire and wish to help them to the fullest
success in their huge and self-sought tasks. They are served
gallantly and industriously by committees, advisers, and friends
innumerable but their task remains, in these sadly complicated
days, all but overwhelming.

It is worth referring to one or two of the special new, and
rather unexpected, problems of leadership today.

The need to be served by scientific specialists of first-class
quality results in the actual field of recruitment often being
unexpectedly limited. High professional qualities may have to
be accepted in place of certain desirable qualities of temperament,
character or experience: there lie possible seeds of trouble.

Expectations have now risen out of all reasonable perspective.
There is a consequent enhanced difficulty in building and maintaining morale. This is a sad but true reflection upon the
modern materialistic world. Happily this regrettable trend is
so far less advanced in Great Britain than elsewhere in the
western world. Though many find difficulty in belief, it is
probably true to say that on polar expeditions there is a greater
correlation between contentment of spirit and humbleness of
living than between contentment and rich material resources.
Further, in the 'services', differences in personal financial status
are acceptable: in private ventures inevitable differences all too
quickly produce a nasty taste.

Another modern problem of peculiar force is fostered by
radio communications. In part it is the same story as in colonial
government yesterday and today—does the Governor govern
or is it the Under-Secretary in Whitehall? In the happy past
the leader and his crew departed and one day returned with
their task well or ill accomplished. Today there is all too much
communication between field and office. Advantages certainly
there are, but there is plenty too in the other scale pan. Radio
communication may provide the leader or the office with facts,
requests and stories, but it rarely provides the essential background of perspective and climate of local feeling and opinion.

The dangers are considerable and cross purposes soon are achieved. The leader's reputation and peace of mind are both liable to suffer.

There are radio repercussions too upon all members of the party. If a parent must die, a job be filled in absence, an engagement broken, better far that the man in the field should receive the shock upon eventual return. Shocks received in isolation are brooded upon, misunderstood or magnified. Again the leader's task in the maintenance of high morale is made more difficult. The marvel, or is it really absurdity, of the direct transmission by radio telephony of a loved female voice, most leaders will agree, is more of a menace than a spur.

In the midst of these complexities we see, now in this decade, perhaps the last of the great private enterprise polar expeditions, subsidised by governments though they may be. With their passing something worthy, even heart-stirring, will have gone, yet some will argue that already they are anachronistic—like an unnationalised railway in modern Britain?

We are now in an age of great national ventures furthering national policies in the polar regions as elsewhere. Some are continuing state enterprises like the Russian Administration of the Northern Sea Route, or our own Falkland Islands Dependencies Survey, or the newly-founded Antarctic section answerable direct to the United States Operations Co-ordination Board. All these and others, Canadian, Australian, French, Danish, Norwegian, Argentine, Chilean, are concerned now with actual or desired long-term occupation based upon a variety of motives. The diverse organisation and leadership of the many national scientific efforts, in connection with the International Geophysical Year of 1957-58, may perhaps most accurately be described as a temporary evolutionary sideline. The main stream is now that of the great state enterprises with their aircraft, their thousands of tons of shipping, and their ability to call upon the full resources of the state in finance, materials and personnel.

Deserving of special comment is that one truly international scientific venture, the Norwegian-British-Swedish Antarctic Expedition 1949-52. Great scientific success attended it: the motivation was a true scientific idealism: there was state subsidisation yet the whole was free from bureaucracy and on a scale sufficiently small for real efficiency to flourish: and the political element, though present, was subdued.   Would that this venture could become the pattern for the future.

Chapter VIII

Polar Prospect Today

"It is unfortunate, considering that enthusiasm moves the world, that so few enthusiasts can be trusted to speak the truth."—(A. J. Balfour.)

ENOUGH has now been said, at least in a short book not designed for the specialist alone, about the life, the environment and the mechanics of polar ventures. We have now passed in mid-century in Antarctica from the solitary expedition to continuous occupation as an aspect of national policy. That stage was reached long ago in the Arctic, where obvious economic factors and the proximity of populous land have for centuries influenced the mode and scale of activity. Now it is proper to investigate further the motivation of present activities in the polar regions for these activities are far greater than ever before. Legal and political factors now play a part which, at any rate in Antarctica, is chiefly, though not wholly, novel.

Using once more the concept of stages in the evolution of polar endeavour, it is largely true to say that the 'pioneer' stage, before the first World War, was the age of real physical difficulty. Economics, scientific and geographical investigation, and the will to find out, were the primary motives in the north, while adventure, even a lurid glamour, played a larger part in the south. National prestige was of great importance in both Arctic and Antarctic. In Antarctica idealism flourished. In the 'transitional' stage, the inter-war years, physical difficulties were greatly diminished, aircraft appeared, personal suffering in exploration nearly disappeared. The chief problems were in finance. Apart from the Russian development of its Northern Sea Route, individuals were ahead of governments in activity, idealism waned and scientific investigation grew in its own right.

Now in the 'modern' stage, since World War II, governments and their agencies are paramount: legal, political and strategic factors have sprung into a previously unimagined prominence;

and developing science is often used as a convenient cloak for much that is of national importance but is certainly not scientific. All things now seem possible, given the resources of men and material, which means people and money. The U.S.A. and U.S.S.R. dominate the scene in both north and south.

The three stages, as we have seen, are not fully separable but they are convenient aids to understanding. There is in each the seed of the next stage, and each contains the vestiges of the last. Was strategy entirely absent in the days of the North-West and North-East Passage efforts? Private idealism and adventure are not yet dead—and long may they live.

The survivors from the polar 'pioneer' stage often find themselves out of sympathy and not conversant with the 'modern' phase. In like manner the surviving heroes of first World War command are ill at ease amid the technicalities of the atomic age of warfare. They are admired and their experience may be useful still in considering generalities. Man is the longest lived of all the mammals (the average life of elephants being no more) and this very fact creates its own great problems in matters of statesmanship, both technical and otherwise, in so fast a changing world. In such ways the polar regions follow the general pattern.

The rapid recent evolution in polar affairs may well be portrayed by quoting from this book's predecessor published in 1939. The same author, younger by nearly two decades, idealistic, a scientist, naïve perhaps but writing words which then seemed acceptable and sensible, wrote thus:

> From his racial infancy and from his individual infancy man has been intensely curious, desiring to know and to find out the why and wherefore of every object around him. In early days of history, man's constant queries, real or unconscious, mostly went unanswered right through the individual lifetime, and now, though our knowledge is so vastly fuller, our mounting desire to know (curiosity is too vulgar a term) has grown to such proportions that the questions seeking answer are all the more abundant.
>
> This desire to know and find out is the driving force behind all pure research, the reward of which is but the answering of a few, and the posing of a multitude of further problems. Nansen said: 'It is to no purpose to discuss the use of knowledge, man wants to know, and when he ceases to do so he is no longer man.' Coupled with the pure desire to know are such fine aims as bettering the lot of others, curing sickness

and preventing ill, though often there are other aims less laudable, such as the acquirement of riches or personal advancement.

The value of any information gained from pure research cannot truly be assessed. But attempts are made to do so, either by examining the extent to which the new information makes clearer the interpretation of facts previously observed, or by the standard of wealth or power obtained. Such has been the motive behind polar exploration, and by these standards have the fruits of expeditions been judged. Just as in the individual the higher faculties and qualities take time to develop to their fullest, so it has been with the history of polar exploration. It was the desire for riches that drove Martin Frobisher to the north-west, but it was a combined patriotism and search after pure knowledge that carried Scott to the South Pole. In its present state polar exploration is adolescent: the search after knowledge becomes more and more the impelling force, but still there is the constant demand for immediate gain, from those not directly involved in the search itself.

There are some who ardently desire to seek out the mysteries of the polar regions, knowing that it is man's duty to discover the distribution of land and sea upon this globe, to understand the formation of its rocks, and the numbers and kinds of animals and plants that live in these distant places. A few wish to go to the extremities of the earth simply for the excitement and experience. But the bulk of the world's population is in poverty, and prevented from thinking of anything beyond its immediate surroundings by the stress of circumstance and the lack of education. Many of those not held back by poverty desire little beyond acquiring more wealth and greater comfort. These are the people who, having no real interest in intelligent achievement and progress, are yet a drag upon the advance of others. Though these people will sometimes help forward the cause of polar exploration if they can be convinced of an immediate prospect of personal gain, very rarely will they help if the gain, though certain, is more remote and less directly personal. So it comes about that the forwarding of polar research is dependent upon the support of learned societies of men and women interested in research from the intellectual standpoint, and of rich patrons, men and business firms, who have either a realisation of things higher than immediate gain in money, or who are wise enough to take a longer risk, and able to see the prospect of a more distant reward. Just as the real beauty of a great cathedral and its value to the worshippers cannot fully be appreciated without an effort of imagination while it is still in the building, so are the value and results of polar exploration at the present time, clearly apparent to those who make the effort to understand, yet hidden from the common run of people.

Some years ago the objects of polar exploration were more clearly defined in the national mind; they were the actual attainment of the Poles. Now the days of 'pole-hunting' (except by aeroplane) are over, but while they lasted the cause of polar exploration did take a big stride forward. The impelling force then was largely national glory, a motive which, though not the highest of all, is far above the simple desire for power and wealth. Even today very many people still believe that polar exploration is directly concerned with nothing beyond this attainment of one or the other extremity of the earth. But with others the mercenary spirit is again in the ascendant. Some can see that there may be money in geographical exploration and accurate mapping, and think perhaps of the modern Russian usage of the North-East Passage. Others think in terms of mineral wealth, and remember with envy the gold of the Yukon. Some expect immediate profit from the slaughter of animals for their fur and blubber, some even thinking they would have the common-sense, were their wishes fulfilled, to conserve the stock and kill only the surplus, thus showing themselves superior to their forbears.

Gradually, however, there is growing up the higher ideal, of polar exploration being one of the many methods by which natural phenomena can be observed and studied, so to increase the sum of man's understanding of his environment. Then, bit by bit, even as it is beginning at the present time, this new knowledge, spread over the many different branches of science will be used by men, grown more sensible than they are today, to bring a fuller and more happy life to all.

This is the idealism that is the eventual goal, but what precisely at the present time does a polar expedition intend to do when it sets out from home? In the past such a question could be more simply answered and more simply understood by the uninitiated. The ship's company sailed away into the unknown, and whatever land they met with, and almost anything they saw, was a direct contribution to the general sum of information. At the same time there were great chances that the voyage would lead to an almost immediate access of wealth in one way or another. Since those days the general increase and widening of knowledge has meant that the 'extensive' method of exploration and research has gradually developed into the 'intensive.' Now it is the turn of the specialist, going out fully equipped to deal with particular problems in various branches of science where the advance of knowledge will be aided by research in polar regions. Here the physicist, geologist, glaciologist, meteorologist and biologist, all have their parts to play, although the work of the geographer and map-maker is of primary importance in unexplored regions. The chances of immediate access to wealth for the few as a direct outcome of a polar expedition are fast dwindling, but more important results, less tangible but for the eventual good of all, are rapidly accumulating with the fuller understanding of Nature and her methods.

As the motives behind polar exploration and the kinds of work involved have changed in the course of time, there has been a corresponding change in the type of person required for the work. At first there were the private adventurers seeking their own profit. Then came the great merchant companies, such as the Muscovy and Hudson Bay Companies, and private firms like Enderby Brothers, whose resourceful and energetic captains, Weddell, Biscoe and others, were filled with a true scientific zeal, in addition to their task of finding out new sources of commercial gain. Later came naval expeditions, their officers charged with a definite scientific mission, but including in their company such specialised scientists as the botanists Banks and Hooker, who voyaged with Cook and Ross. Gradually it became apparent that naval officers, however efficient, could not be expected to cope with the more specialised scientific problems. So more recently has come the transition to expeditions comparatively small in size, but including a large number of young men specially trained in the various branches of science. Soon this change will go further for, with the advance of knowledge, the opportunities and facilities for a particular study in any area will more accurately be known in advance, so bringing into the field scientists still more experienced. At present men of standing cannot for the most part afford the risk of disappointment in their work, but as soon as assurance can be given on this point, the scope of polar exploration will be magnified by their efforts. This new stage has already begun, but it cannot advance far until the principle is realised in exploration that, up to a point and with proper management, a doubling of expenditure may bring far more than double results in the information gained. Also it should be remembered that though junior men at the beginning of their careers may be able and ready to forgo all remuneration, this sacrifice is not possible for all scientific workers, and can hardly be expected from those in established positions.

Though in the future scientists of greater skill than ever before will carry out research in polar lands, the environment they study will be the same as in the past. Though their equipment and mode of life may undergo many changes, these will be governed by the same environmental influences as at present. These environmental influences and man's physical and mental reactions to them are of permanent interest.

Now so much is changed: the whole scale of activity is so tremendous that past efforts seem puny. A single Russian Antarctic expedition in early 1956 landed nearly 10,000 tons of stores, an amount which probably surpassed the total of all Antarctic expeditions together previous to 1925. An American naval task force did likewise ten years earlier. Today the prize goes to the nation which has the will and the material resources to be committed in greatest quantity. The U.S.A. sends in scores of ships in a year to her strategic air base in north-west Greenland, Thule, which has no more than a six-week shipping season. Russia has over a hundred meteorological stations disposed along her northern shore, and lands four-engined aircraft regularly on wheels on the north polar pack to victual further floating stations. The U.S.A. has already set up a substantial scientific station at the South Pole which is victualled from the air. She has already sent twice weekly flights from Alaska to the North Pole regularly for a decade.

Nothing seems physically impossible. Great hangars at 77°
North are heated by oil-fired steam from −40° C. to + 20° C.
so that the mechanics can work upon the aircraft in comfortable
undress. The Americans fly aircraft direct from New Zealand
to the Ross Ice Shelf and the Russians think little of flights
inland at mid-winter towards the south magnetic pole to cheer
a mechanically equipped surface sledge party. Other nations,
likewise, in proportion to their political interest, legal or
usurping, plus healthy scientific stimulation and perhaps too a
remnant of the spice of adventure, perform lesser feats, but all
prodigies by earlier standards.

Idealism is well-nigh dead, adventure moribund and certainly
vestigial. Economic and practical uses are fundamental to the
further development of the Russian Northern Sea Route, and to
some young enterprises in Alaska and the Canadian Arctic.
Elsewhere the economic spur to polar activity is in general of
minor import. The International Whaling Convention adequately, even admirably and surprisingly, still oversees the
exploitation of the Southern Ocean, a cheering reminder and
result of the idealistic scientific efforts of the inter-war years in
which Great Britain played a most notable part.

The stimulus of desire for ever speedier transport promotes
a variety of Arctic air routes via great circle courses between the
centres of densest population. In this the Scandinavian
countries have recently made great advances as operational
pioneers. Young men from Britain in the early thirties pointed
the way as amateur prophets and junior demonstrators in
Greenland. Much further development is to be expected,
though the intrinsic difficulties of highest latitude navigation
and the hazards of too infrequent emergency landing grounds
will long exert their influence. On the other hand so little of
the world's population lives in the southern hemisphere, and
the few great cities are in such low latitudes, that trans-Antarctic
commercial flying is for long improbable.

Polar science remains and grows apace to gianthood. Only
a small fraction, if any, of the Arctic now remains unportrayed
with fair accuracy on maps drawn from aerial photographic
reconnaissances. The same is likely to be true of the whole of

Antarctica within the next five years, though the adequacy of ground control may be somewhat less. Apart from basic survey, meteorology and geology have twin pride of place in polar science today. Both are stimulated by directly practical needs, or greeds in the case of geology. A much smaller, but healthy brother science, is glaciology, with the interest centred on the physical properties and regimes of snow and ice, notably in Greenland and Antarctica.

The meteorologists have two directly practical spurs to effort. The first is concerned with the fundamental understanding of the movements of air masses, together with the problems, practices and possibilities of weather forecasting. There is here great scope for joint effort in both Arctic and Antarctic, and the degree of co-ordination already in being with the aid of the World Meteorological Organisation is substantial indeed.

The second particular present effort of meteorologists in high latitudes, more particularly in Antarctica where so far there is less knowledge, is in the study of the upper air. An early practical, though beastly, aspect is concerned with judgments of the drift, dispersal and duration of radio-active dust clouds following explosions real or hypothetical.

Polar geologists are in general direct seekers after mineral wealth. Proofs of its improbability in particular areas are important too so that efforts may be concentrated elsewhere. Aerial photography, flights with instruments of geophysical investigation, brief landings from helicopters, exploratory parties flown in by transport aircraft or arriving by tractor trains, are but stages in the geological progress. Arctic geological exploration has made immense advances in the last decade, while the like intense investigation of Antarctica is the programme for the next. The northern nations directly concerned are four, while in Antarctica more numerous are those with aspirations.

The practical glaciologists are primarily concerned with ice in three aspects: as a hindrance to navigation at sea; as an indicator of climatic fluctuations; and as a covering to what may be geologically important. The development of the Russian

Northern Sea Route in the thirties, and of victualling by sea of stations north of the American continent in the last decade, follow from some amelioration of climate coinciding with the development of superior icebreaking ships of ever greater power. Along the Russian Northern Sea Route the last ten years has probably witnessed a small climatic swing in the opposite direction which so far is of no practical importance, at least in the face of still improving technical resources.

The world's ice sheets, predominantly that of Antarctica, plus the far smaller Greenland, contain enough ice so that, if melted, sea level throughout the world would rise by something over one hundred feet. It may be observed that a very substantial proportion of the world's population and the majority of its great cities would thereby be swamped. But melting at an embarrassing rate is so improbable that we can view the prospect with complete equanimity. Likewise it is asserted, by those trained and capable of such calculations, that incredible numbers of hydrogen bombs would be needed to set free significant quantities of water.

These scientific aspirations have long played their part, but a powerful newcomer in the motivation of polar endeavour is military strategy. This is a phenomenon mostly of the present decade, earlier thoughts on this subject being premature until the technical development of aircraft had reached an advanced stage. Now the DEW (Distant Early Warning) radar line of the North American continent, together with its offshoots and corollaries, from the Aleutian Islands to north Greenland, is the mainspring of Arctic activity in the New World. Comparable Russian activities, less publicised, perhaps less spectacular, but presumed no less effective, are strung out along the Eurasian shore and its northern island groups. This too, in maintenance, is a feature of the Russian Northern Sea Route with its series of powerful icebreakers leading the summer convoys of freighters. Russia and North America alike put in from east and west each open season great and vigorous victualling expeditions to maintain in a state of preparedness their northern stations. With increased range and speed of aircraft the strategic and tactical almost merge. But fundamental, it

WEASELS TOWING THE "CABOOSE" AND LOADED CARGO SLEDGES DURING A SEISMIC JOURNEY

(*Photograph by C. W. M. Swithinbank, "Norwegian–British–Swedish Antarctic Expedition, 1949–52"*)

A NORSEMAN REFUELLING A SNOWMOBILE ON THE FROZEN SURFACE OF A LAKE

is, that the potentially hostile major population centres are in closest proximity via Arctic great circle routes.

In Antarctica strategic considerations yet have less force: vastness, lack of inhabitants, climate and ice join to retard excitement. There is appreciation however in some quarters that with the world as it is today there is danger, anywhere, in letting the other fellow gain a foothold, so that parallel activity develops like an arms race. More generally understandable perhaps is the vulnerability of the Panama canal. The dangers and narrowness of the Straits of Magellan are obvious to all, so that Drake Passage, the 700 mile wide strait between Cape Horn and the South Shetland Islands off Antarctica at once assumes importance. This Passage is the single constriction in the world-encircling Southern Ocean. Its surveillance and control could so easily become of paramount significance. And immediately to its south is the only yet conceivable site for an Antarctic naval base, Deception Island, the 'capital' of the British Falkland Islands Dependencies, and the whaling centre of the earlier decades of this century. Deception Island on the fringe of the Antarctic Peninsula in long. 61° W. and lat. 63° S., and the French Iles de Kerguelen in long. 69° E. and lat. 49° S. in mid-Southern Ocean, possess the only two known considerable natural harbours open for a large portion of the year.

Legal titles, curiosities and concepts are of particular significance in both Arctic and Antarctic in these present days. This is no legal treatise so that it is fair but to indicate the kind of problem which already has or soon will exercise the minds of international and other legal pundits. In the Arctic there is now virtually no international doubt as to land ownership, the result of long occupation, proximity to temperate land masses, or other factors. The Hague Court arbitration in 1933 awarded East Greenland to Denmark. Svalbard is under Norwegian sovereignty but with special privileges for a group of treaty-signing nations. All known northern lands, and new discoveries are now no longer expectable, are territories whose sovereignty is clear. Nevertheless each northernmost land claims all to the north lying between its own bounding lines of longitude

H

extended to the pole. Each claims any land that might be found and has an emotional attachment or presumed sphere of influence in these same converging marine sectors. What then if an American- or Russian-occupied ice-borne floating meteorological station drifts in its polar wanderings into the other's region of interest? The legal, indeed the practical, mind can envisage many possibilities. So far the drifting stations, whether on 'ice islands' or on normal floes, have behaved with decorum or have been abandoned before moving into contentious regions.

In Antarctica festering sores of political contention remain. The continent has been divided politically into sectors, bounded by lines of longitude converging on the pole. The sectors have political ownership based, fundamentally, on priority of discovery backed, in international law, by later occupation, administration and provision of facilities suitable to a territory that is uninhabited and difficult of access. Britain, Australia, New Zealand, France and Norway have mutually recognised sovereign powers and contiguous sectors. One wide South Pacific sector remains unclaimed, and to it the United States has a better basis for a claim than any: but she as yet has made no claim despite the discoveries and pressures of her bold citizens, and likewise has not recognised the claims of others. Argentina and Chile have over-lapping claims to the British Falkland Islands Dependencies but have refused to accept arbitration of any kind by the Hague Court. Their claims are weak on legal grounds. But these usurpers, and those other world powers which have not formally recognised the sovereignty in law of the initial five, seem now to wait and watch. They extend their activities on others' sovereign territory, and have little stimulus to accept a final division of the continent based on the tradition of international law. Rather do they seem to hope for a political solution, of yet unstated kind, based on power, bargaining, proximity, and present day activity. The next decade in Antarctica may well provide great change, bitterness, and decrease of the prestige of international law, besides the excitements of new discoveries in science.

In this whole connection it is a fact, of considerable practical

E ANTARCTIC

showing

ATIONS AT THE DATE OF PUBLICATION OF THIS BOOK

with the start of the International Geophysical Year)

NORWAY

andwich | 26 Kronprinsesse Märtha Kyst.

ads.
Shetland

SOUTH AFRICA

n Island, | 27 Marion Island, Prince Edward Islands.
28 Gough Island.
29 Tristan da Cunha.

go.
Coast.
Islands,

UNITED KINGDOM

30 Stanley, Falkland Islands.
31 Grytviken, South Georgia.
32 Signy Island (Base H), South Orkney Islands.
33 Admiralty Bay (Base G), King George Island, South Shetland Islands.
34 Deception Island (Base B), South Shetland Islands.
35 Hope Bay (Base D), Trinity Peninsula.
36 View Point, Duse Bay, Trinity Peninsula.
37 Port Lockroy (Base A), Palmer Archipelago.
38 Argentine Islands (Base F), off Graham Coast.
39 "Lent Island" (Base W), Loubet Coast.
40 Horseshoe Island (Base Y), Marguerite Bay, off Fallieres Coast.
41 Halley Bay (Royal Society base), Caird Coast.
42 "Shackleton" (Trans-Antarctic Expedition base), Filchner Ice Shelf.

Shetland | 43 "South Ice."

Shetland

UNITED STATES

Shetland | 44 "Little America 5," Kainan Bay, Ross Ice Shelf.
45 "Byrd Station," Marie Byrd Land.

l, South | 46 South Geographical Pole.
47 "Ellsworth Station," Filchner Ice Shelf.

l, Trinity | 48 "Wilkes Station," Vincennes Bay, Wilkes Land.
49 "Williams Air Operations Facility," Ross Island, Ross

lise Har- | Ice Shelf (operational support base).

UNITED STATES/NEW ZEALAND

50 "Adare Station," Cape Hallett, Victoria Land.

Adélie.
Adélie.

U.S.S.R.

51 "Mirnyy," Queen Mary Land.
52 *"Vostok," South Geomagnetic Pole area, Wilkes Land.
53 *"Sovetskaya," area of so-called "Pole of Relative Inaccessibility," Enderby Land.
54 "Pionerskaya," Queen Mary Land (operational support base).
55 *"Komsomolskaya," Princess Elizabeth Land (operational support base).

Shelf. | 56 "Oazis," Queen Mary Land.

* Proposed stations.

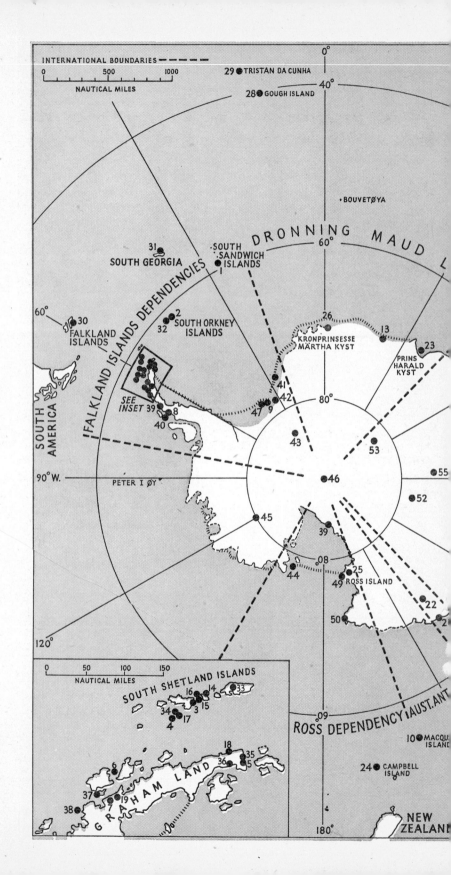

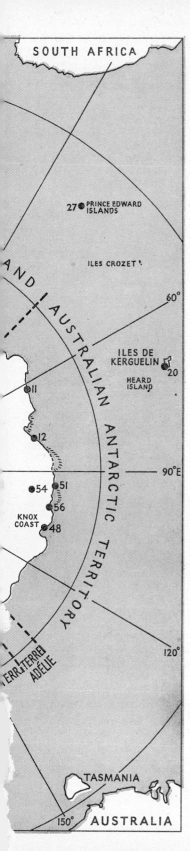

INTERNATIONAL GEOPHYSICAL YEAR S

(which corresponds approximate

ARGENTINA

1. *"Teniente Esquivel," Thule Island, South
   Islands.
2. "Orcadas," Laurie Island, South Orkney Isl
3. "Teniente Camara," Half Moon Island, Soutl
   Islands.
4. "Decepción" or "Primero de Mayo," Decept
   South Shetland Islands.
5. "Esperanza," Hope Bay, Trinity Peninsula.
6. "Melchior," Gamma Island, Palmer Archipe
7. "Almirante Brown," Paradise Harbour, Dan
8. "General San Martin," Barry Island, Debenha
   off Fallieres Coast.
9. "General Belgrano," Filchner Ice Shelf.

AUSTRALIA

10. Macquarie Island.
11. Mawson, Mac-Robertson Land.
12. Davis, Princess Elizabeth Land.

BELGIUM

13. *Breidvika, Prinsesse Ragnhild Kyst.

CHILE

14. *Coppermine Cove, Robert Island, South
    Islands.
15. "Arturo Prat," Greenwich Island, South
    Islands.
16. *Yankee Harbour, Greenwich Island, South
    Islands.
17. "Pedro Aguirre Cerda," Deception Islan
    Shetland Islands.
18. "General Bernardo O'Higgins," Cape Legoup
    Peninsula.
19. "Presidente Gabriel Gonzales Videla," Para
    bour, Danco Coast.

FRANCE

20. Port-aux-Français, Iles de Kerguelen.
21. "Dumont d'Urville," Pointe Géologie, Terre
22. "Charcot," South Magnetic Pole area, Terre

JAPAN

23. "Showa Base," Prins Harald Kyst.

NEW ZEALAND

24. Campbell Island.
25. "Scott," Pram Point, Ross Island, Ross Ice

indeed political significance, that of the five mutually recognising sovereign powers in Antarctica (Britain, Australia, New Zealand, France and Norway) not one is owner of an icebreaker, while the political usurper (Argentina) and the great contenders (U.S.A. and Russia) are all provided with a freedom of the southern seas which the sovereign owners do not possess. Is it, among the five, poverty, lack of foresight, a kindly unreality based on conditions before the first World War, or what which has held them back from equipping themselves properly to meet the challenge of today?

It should not pass unremarked that the first and only shots so far fired in anger in Antarctica were in 1952, when Argentines attempted to affright a British party at Hope Bay in our Falkland Islands Dependencies, which we have continually occupied now since 1943. In that region the last dozen years have seen what might be termed a 'base-race' between Britain, Argentina and Chile attempting to strengthen claims by tiny occupations and the establishment of post offices. In fact Britain's formal claim to the area was made in 1908.

Against this background, those whose eyes are open view the present and coming scientific activities connected with the Antarctic aspects of the International Geophysical Year 1957-58. On good scientific grounds there is reason for great endeavour. But some scientists quickly realised how favourable was the opportunity for obtaining the necessary support and monies from the political leaders of their own countries. And some political leaders quickly realised how hidden ambitions could long be cloaked by scientific research before an overt move is made. The few have had the wakeful foresight, the rest repose in their research. This year of 1957 is the turning point in Antarctic history. What will have emerged a decade hence? Will it be a universal acceptance of the rights of the present five mutually recognising sovereign powers or still a period of claim and counter-claim? Will there have been settlement by a new carving of the continent into new sovereign areas, or an agreement over spheres of influence? Or will there have arrived some acceptable form of condominium or internationalisation, however ill-defined and however unpromising those concepts at present so often are?   The most, that the rash prophet can with fair confidence assert, is that political factors will largely have prevailed over the claims of international law as at present understood.

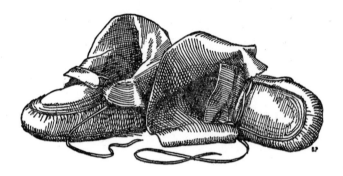

WALRUS HUNT (AFTER OLAUS MAGNUS, 1555)

CHAPTER IX

Memories

FACTS, principles and politics can be appreciated by those who have never journeyed into high latitudes, but there are other aspects of these regions that can never be realised to the full until a man has been there for himself. Since all cannot go to garner experience, an attempt must be made to convey to others something of the fascination, the peace, beauty, solitude and other special attributes of these lands. From descriptions of places, scenes and memories, and by comparing and contrasting, those at home may at least perceive some part of the reality of polar lands. Pain and discomfort, anxiety and fear, fade into the past, but beauties and pleasures, excitement and wonder, are remembered, their intensity growing with the passage of time.

The three friends lie at peace upon the hillside, filled with the joy of life. Around them the night-long sunset fills the sky with colours, scarlet and orange, yellow and deepest blue. Their

107

couch too is bright with autumn tints, the crimson, russet and golden leaves of the creeping birch and willow, and the deep purple-red of the crowberries. Below them is the fjord, still and blue, set with pack ice gently drifted with the tide, while scattered bergs reflect the light in their green and turquoise cracks and grottoes. Beyond are the ice-mantled peaks and snow-fields never trodden by men. Though it is long past midnight the friends wait on in happy contemplation. On the beach is their tent, and beside it rises the smoke of their camp fire burning driftwood, the bountiful gift of the great Siberian rivers so many thousands miles away. Their boat lies at anchor, swinging slowly in an eddy. The silence is unbroken but for sounds that come gently one by one. Geese fly overhead, the swish and creak of their feathers pulsing through the air long after they are past. The calls of the divers come from across the fjord, clangorous and loving, the birds yet seeming on their honeymoon, though their full-fledged chicks swim beside them. A Musk Ox, browsing, moves slowly across the hillside; a dainty Arctic Fox, with nimble feet, trots along the shore line. The three friends continue their silent contemplation as the rising sun creeps sideways from behind the hills.

That is polar peace.

But the quality of peace is not the sole prerogative of polar lands. Perfect peace reigns on a desert shore. It is evening, and the sun is setting behind the hills twenty miles away across the level desert. The sea is calm and a gentle wind from the north is cool after the heat of the day. Out at sea a sudden smack tells of a giant ray that has for a moment flung itself clear of the water, in joy or anguish no man knows. The nimble shore crabs with stalked eyes upraised patter in platoons along the tide line. Over the reef a hawking osprey drops with outstretched claws, snatches a coral fish and flies triumphant shoreward to the ancient pile of debris that is her nest. The sun sinks lower; it is the time for prayer. The passing Arab couches his camel, and together kneeling on the desert sand, he bows his head towards the city of the prophet's birth.

Such is January on the desert coast. January in the Antarctic has its own peculiar joys in scenery and life. A small three-masted schooner comes slowly under engines down the straits. The sun shines from a cloudless sky. On either side the all-mantling ice ends in fringing cliffs, only the topmost peaks and sea-washed islands expose the naked rock. Drifting floes and sparkling bergs float upon the still blue waters. Flocks of feeding penguins, like jumping fish, dart outward from the cleaving bow. Petrels circle low in swinging sweeps around the ship, their outspread wings seeming to skim the surface. Great whales, singly and in schools, rise blowing, some under the quarter, others as far as the eye can see up and down the strait. In the upward surge the full length of their pelican mouths is seen, then turning for the downward plunge a fluked tail may wave aloft. Silvery seals, singly and in groups, with blinking eyes of wonder lie upon the floes. Slowly they raise their dog-like heads to examine this strange ship as she passes, then yawn and stretch their toes with sleepy pleasure. There is a hum in the southern sky, and a small yellow seaplane, shining brightly from its every part, glides down towards the ship. It circles once and lands astern. A line is thrown, and two men come aboard; greetings pass and an exchange of news. Soon the plane moves once more swiftly across the water, altering her course to avoid the spouting whales. She rises and turns towards base, leaving the following ship far, far behind.

The months pass quickly and soon it is August again, at the end of the southern winter. The sun sweeps low over the mountains, and his warmth is just perceptible. The men feel a wonderful elation, their spirits rise with joy, not fully realising their former deprivation until the sun's return. Running behind the sledges they shout to the dogs as they cross the last shadow and burst into the new light. The dogs too are cheered, and break into a gallop, with ears pricked and plumed tails waving like banners above them. They bound over the wind-crusted ice, breath-clouds trailing with their shadows behind them. Ahead stretches the white plain of the fjord, with pinnacles of ice dancing in the low mirage. To the left the mountain cliffs are in shadow, but on the peaks little clouds of golden drift stand as haloes. On the right all is glittering brilliance, red rock summits, divided by great glaciers, each more stepped than the pyramid at Sakkara. The crevasses and ice faces gleam with ocean blues and greens, and above rides the full-moon, clear with yellow light. The sun moves a little to the west of north, and sinking once more from sight, slides behind a distant berg with a parting flash of brilliant green. That is joy and grandeur.

Both in life and death the seals play a very special part in many polar lands.

James sculled gently over the stern and smoked his pipe. Brian was in the bow with an ice pick. I sat with a rifle amidships. Our quarry was a large Leopard Seal lying on a stranded ice floe at the tip of the island. We wanted, in particular, her skull and ovaries besides her meat. To get the skull undamaged, a killing shot in the neck was needed, a shot from a ·303 with a blunt-nosed or filed-tip bullet. A shot at short range too was needed because she might wriggle off the floe and then sink in the deep channel if we were not quickly up to her. So we came near, quietly by water, as she slept.

The sea was calm and the movement of the scattered streams of brash ice was by tidal currents rather than by wind. The sun cast blue shadows on the whiteness of the floe tops, and their cracks and crannies and their underwater fringes were translucent green. Green too were the small moss patches on the islands forming the creek sides, but this green was dull and spotted with brown, some deadness and some the little tufts of tiny upstanding fruiting bodies of the moss itself. Round about the moss patches the skuas had their nests, and the birds circled overhead with loud cries of disapproval and protest. Their wheeling agitation was no concern of ours, just as it had no novelty or import to the tiny Wilson's Petrels in their tunnel nests hollowed out beneath those self-same moss tussocks. Our quarry was that Leopard Seal, and our pleasure was life that afternoon. Life and intended death were mingled with great peace and beauty, beauty which reigned from the calm water with its feeding penguins, upwards over the hazy yet glistening ice-cloaked mountains to the sky above, piled high with slowly curling clouds.

So we moved gently down the creek towards our Leopard Seal. She lay on her chest, her back dark and dry, her streaked and spotted belly hidden on the ice, and her horse-large head and neck stretched out in front. But Leopard Seals are wary beasts, so different from the other species of the south. She heard us coming and with a wriggle and a heave she slipped into the water. We were not to be the dealers of death that day. She was swiftly gone and for 30 yards remained beneath the surface. Then she showed her head and swam at the surface, leaving behind her a wake which washed along and lapped under the over-hanging ice foot of the island on the left. Her whole movement was a demonstration of power and speed and controlled energy and strength. She seemed to force the waters apart and ride over them rather than divide them and move through them like the other seals.

Onward she swam and right out of the creek into the wide sea beyond. We had failed in our hunt, but now that Leopard Seal was to show us, instead, her prowess as a huntress. Where we had come by stealth she relied on speed and a penguin was her quarry. Any penguin would do , and the quicker the better. She rushed towards the nearest feeding group, 100 yards away, swimming and bobbing like diving ducks. Keeping at the surface there was no mistaking her purpose and the penguins fled. Their technique of attempted escape was like that of the shoals of glistening fish in tropic seas, hoping, one might say, by keeping above the surface to escape the sharp fangs beneath. By alternate 10 ft. leaps above the surface and 10 ft. swims beneath, they strove to follow a sinuous course to security. At first they fled ahead in a compact body, leaping together and swimming together. Then as our leopard came up with them they suddenly broke formation, scattered sideways, and were seen by us no more.

The leopard stopped, now 200 yards ahead of us, and there in her mouth, held by the sharp pointed canines and the trident molars, struggled and squawked the penguin which had lost life's race. It struggled for a moment but that was all, the next job was the leopard's. She shook that penguin with great violence from side to side, swiftly like a terrier with a rat. The terrier shakes to kill, but the Leopard Seal shakes for another purpose. In a moment the wretched penguin was shaken from its skin. A dull red carcase, complete with head and limbs and frills of skin, was flung through the air. This was the leopard's meal, and she swallowed it with swiftness, and swam away. She had shown us how to hunt. Our only capture was the penguin's ragged skin, torn, black and white, and smeared with blood.

Peace and beauty still reigned: the sea continued calm, and James sculled gently over the stern and smoked his pipe. One penguin was dead and one Leopard Seal had fed.

A Weddell Seal met another fate. Smooth and black she was, long yet plump. We saw her stretched out there in the distance, asleep and alone. She would meet our need, for our dogs and we were cold and hungry after long travel. So we killed her, all unsuspecting in the silence and the evening sunlight. The rifle shot echoed and re-echoed from the ice cliffs: the dogs whined and pawed in ecstatic expectation.

First, swift decapitation. Then I split that sleek black seal right down her belly, from blood-hissing neck seven feet down to the vent. I used my knife with skill, for many had suffered the same sad but necessary fate. The three inch blubber parted softly from the blade, and the skin and hair made a slight sibilant sound as the edge ran swiftly through. Then I cut the thin belly wall and, with firm strength and a slight wriggling movement of the knife, I cleaved my way through the full length of the sternum. That needs deftness, to carry the blade just where the cartilage is soft. Next a strong sweeping slash along each side of the thorax from within, half cutting through the ribs so that the two sides of the chest would lie back flat.

The transformation was complete. A minute before that plump, smooth, unoffending seal lay at peace on the glistening snow, beside her exit from the deep dark waters of the fjord below. Now she was a split and scarlet kipper, half a ton of flesh flattened on the ice, her heart still beating strongly in the centre and her muscles quivering as I cut them. But we and our dogs were cold and hungry and in need of what that seal alone could give.

When I started to work my hands seemed frozen, but now, handling the flesh and dipping into the hot pools of blood, the first scalding sensation passed and I felt the pleasure of soothing warmth. So I carved her and fed the grateful dogs while my companion pitched the tent and made all ready for the night. Her fine thick loin muscles, great solid lumps of dark red meat, were food for men: so were her liver, her heart and her tongue. The flesh of her back and sides and limbs would go to feed the dogs in the coming weeks and her blubber likewise. All these I stored in boxes. By morning the flesh would be in massive frozen bricks, brittle when chopped, and the blubber would be yellowish pink and waxy. Some of her liver, about 5 lb. of the best pieces from the edges of the massive lobes, I put apart. In an hour's time we would be frying them in margarine over the Primus inside the tent. We would fill our empty stomachs with half-cooked liver, soft as butter. A candle would light our meal, and we would lick our lips and fry some more.

The dismemberment was done. The sun was low, blood-red above the distant ice horizon: the dogs already slept replete, curled into balls on the hard snow. We completed our pre-parations for the night, then looked what we had wrought. That peaceful seal was turned into food and colour. The remnants of her carcase were a gaunt and ruddy framework. Her blood had congealed into a pitted, gory mass in the ice beneath her. The entrails lay in a coiled, disreputable heap. The level sea ice stretched into the distance, walled by cliffs and mountains, glistening white, suffused with pink. The sun, a scarlet globe, was sinking slowly and slantwise beneath the horizon. In the foreground was that wreck, a seal which we had used to meet our pressing need, yet still in colour harmony, scarlet amid the white.

Mingled with memories is the appreciation of contrasts, and in a way these are the spice of life. "When every one is somebody, then no one's anybody." Take those two contrasted states, the completest solitude and the grossest of overcrowding which are sometimes strangely intermingled and yet both can be enjoyed. Though the population per square mile in a polar land is infinitesimally small, the population per small room is often enormous, as crowded as a slum. Consider the surroundings without, and the occupations within, the typical house of a polar expedition.* Outside there is a vast continent, far larger than Europe, completely devoid of human inhabitants. Within, the room is perhaps 14 ft. by 20 ft. and some 6½ ft. high, and round the walls are ranged bunks, each filled with a man's personal belongings, books and clothes on shelves, pipe racks, guns, dog whips and harnesses, a tooth brush on a hook, and photographs of home and friends. One bunk is clean and tidy, another little better than a pile of litter, in which the owner nestles like a ferret. One man prefers to sleep exposed to the public gaze, while another attempts to shut himself off with wood and curtains. The floor is moderately clean, the ceiling timbered and low. A stove, tables and chairs occupy the central space. In this room nearly a dozen men are happily spending the evening after dinner. The occupations of the men are various. One is reading with his feet on the stove and loudly playing a gramophone. By his side the day's weather notes are being written by a man smoking a large cigar, while his non-smoking neighbours are coughing violently. At the table are two others, each with a machine. While the one thumps lustily with his fore-fingers on the keys of an ancient typewriter, the other at the sewing machine is patching his dirty clothes, though stoutly maintaining that they are recently washed. The man in the corner is mending dog harnesses which had been in use a few hours before. Alongside is the clinic, where the doctor skilfully delves within the mouth of one suffering from toothache. Beyond the stove there is just room enough for a display of novice skill at hair cutting. One

---

* This refers to pre-World War II conditions in the 'transitional' phase before material standards had risen.

man gets up and passes through to the kitchen to fetch himself an orange drink that wards off scurvy. Inadvertently he clinks his spoon inside his mug, and at once others cry out for him to mix some more. In time the thirsty are satisfied, and at about half past ten a few begin to go to bed. There is a great coming and going and opening of the front door, and those cleaning their teeth pretend to spit upon the back of the naked man who is squatting in a little bath-tub on the kitchen floor. At last all are in their bunks; some read by the light of candles, some sleep, some snore, while one decides that he must leave his bunk once more to make himself another cup of tea. The day is done and peacefully they sleep and dream. . . .

A kestrel, poised on fluttering wings, hangs level with the eyes. Beneath, great trees clothed in their newest coat of spring are as a vast army of giant tortoises, thwarted in desire to climb the steep hillside. Above, the round chalk hills, bare but for the close turf and scattered clumps of gorse, enclose the woods below as does a horseshoe its good luck. Beyond stretches the greenness of England, as far as the eye can carry, green fields, green woodlands and green hills. It is for these that the heart will sometimes long in distant barren lands, the greenness, the trees and the turf. Mosses and lichens, bright saxifrages and willow carpets are beauties in themselves, the poor polar substitutes for the green of England. Of great trees there are none, no oaks, no elms, no poplars pink with catkins, no willows at the water's side, nor beeches on the chalk. Polar plants are of a duller green, short and squat, though often bright with tiny flowers. Even the Arctic forest is but a lowly creeping mat of birch and willow, scarcely ankle high, whose twigs break and crackle as striding feet press upon the tree-tops. The great southern continent has not even these, just a few lichens, fewer mosses, one grass, one tiny pink, but nothing more to represent the greenness of the homeland. But of animals there are polar substitutes in plenty, Musk Oxen and seals may serve for cattle, penguins and ducks for the fowls of the farm, and skuas may pass for rooks. Fish there are, and little beasts that remind the wanderer of pond and meadow; fairy shrimps are polar frogs, and lemmings are the rats and mice.

But whatever the circumstances, peace and security are what men seek. Despite his civilisation man is still a primitive and fearful animal. In the night, when he cannot see, strange fears come upon him, and he seeks a place secluded from the elements and secure from his enemies real and imaginary. Some may conquer all fear of the hours of darkness, but man is at a disadvantage, and the changing emotions of his mind are far stronger than in the sunlight. So in memory, nights of peace and nights of anxiety are the more contrasted one to the other. Could a night be more peaceful than in a desert, far from the dwellings of other? The encampment is in the final bend of a winding wadi, flat-floored with sheer walls of curtained limestone running three hundred feet up into the night. Inland the view is cut short by the walls at another turn, while seawards, the wadi loses itself at the plateau edge and widens upon the coastal plain. Above, the sky is a ribbon of stars framed by the wanderings of the valley below. A dozen camels, couched after the long day's journey, are methodically re-chewing twigs torn from a solitary thorn tree, nourished by a thunderstorm now seven years past. Their masters, already asleep, lie as shapeless bundles round a smouldering fire. At a little distance stands a tent of western pattern, housing two who love each other more than the starlit night. Apart a young man, wrapped in a blanket, lies contemplating the moon as she sweeps across the river of sky. She crosses and the shadow comes: the man turns and lights a naked candle by his pillow, then reads an hour by its still, unflickering light.

Compare this desert peace with the troubles of a night spent on the ice of a polar sea. The ice is yet barely one foot thick. It is mid-winter, and the sun is ever below the horizon. The men lie in their tents fully clothed, prepared to move at an instant signal. Throughout the twilight hours a hurricane wind has raged, threatening to uproot the tents and to expose their human inmates to the blizzard. The dogs in their harnesses lie unmoving, close curled against the drift that lashes round them. During the evening the wind has moderated, but its full effects are still to come. Great bergs may have gained momentum to start them on a course of destruction to the young ice around, or a swell perhaps has been raised that will break vast ice-fields into little pans. As the evening passes, shocks and jars in the ice are perceptible, rather to hips and shoulders as the men lie upon the floorskins than to ears pressed listening to the ground. It is dark, and will be dark for many hours: no retreat towards safety can be made until those hours are past: nothing can be done but hope, and the individual minds are filled with vague plans of possible action in the last extremity of need.

Difficulties now are passed. After a seeming endless struggle through the freshly tumbled pressure, the dogs at last can run at speed over the smooth unbroken ice beyond. The drivers sit upon the sledges, now for the first time able to take in the beauty of the day. It is just past noon, but the sun towards which they journey is below the horizon, his presence known by a blood-red glow filling the north. The cloudless dome of sky, in front is light almost to the zenith, but behind in darkening shades of purest blue is star-lit night. To the north the smooth, hard surface reflects the glow as a further pool of redness, while on either side the upstanding bergs and tumbled ice throw back the colour in points and sparkles. To the east the young moon rides upon the mountain tops, gilding their ice-covered summits with yellow light.

But clear skies and distant views are not essential for appreciation. On a fog-bound island nest multitudes of birds that come and go with seeming ease, finding their way through the gloom with swift precision. It is a watery land, whose surface is covered with numberless barren, shallow lakes, so that the intervening dryness is but a network of earth and stones,

covered in parts with mats of creeping willow, moss and saxifrage.   There is one inland mountain whose flank rises up from
the watery plain.   Once an ancient moving scree, it is now
covered by a moist carpet of luxuriant moss and lichen.   The
moss is bright and pleasing in its greenness, and the quaint
forms of the scarlet fruiting lichens add colour to the contrast.
There is a continual subdued patter of water dripping from rock
to rock beneath the living cover, which itself is sodden as a
sponge.   The cries of birds come from near and far, gulls,
skuas and divers.   Suddenly there is a high-pitched barking
close at hand, and dimly seen in the misty gloom passes a family
of peeping prick-eared Arctic foxes.   They vanish and are
heard again higher up searching among the stones.   Then come
shrill chattering cries of alarm, and the swift beat of stumpy
wings as the multitudinous Little Auks rush from their holes and
circle in dense flocks in the fog above.   Round and round they
fly, uttering again and again their notes of alarm, until at last,
the foxes gone, they can once more creep softly into their
underground homes among the boulders.

There are many memories that dwell for ever in the mind,
but none more clearly lasting than those that record the moments
of greatest joy and wonder.   There stand the mountains in
glistening splendour, clothed and surrounded with ice.   The
sky is cloudless blue, the air is calm and the temperature far, far
down upon the scale.   The watchers stand entranced, as their
eyes, the first of all men's, feast upon the glory that is before
them.   In the great clearness it almost seems that they could
stretch out their hands and touch the rounded smoothness of
the ice-filled corries.   But those sunlit peaks and glaciers are
thirty miles and more away, out of reach save of the eyes alone.
Utter silence reigns: the watchers, as they listen, hear nothing
in their ears but the gentle surge and pulse of their own blood
streaming in its narrow courses.   The pervading sense of
wonder is all-satisfying as they absorb the elemental beauty of
the ice-cloaked earth.   It is as a dream of another planet,
enormous, magnificent, to be seen, not touched, for gods not

men. So still, so silent and so beautiful, "as it was in the beginning, is now and ever shall be, world without end."

Such are the memories that linger, and it is they that give to polar expeditions their one insurmountable defect, the after-feeling, the constant longing to return. The momentary pang of leaving the lands of peace and beauty is quickly conquered by the anticipation of homely pleasures, the re-uniting of the family in love and friendship, the seeing in fact the people so long fancied. Then, arrived, there is the joy and excitement of coming again at last into the home, and seeing again the greenness of the countryside, tall trees and tangled hedgerows, mown lawns and the flowery beds of formal gardens. There are constant smaller pleasures, warm friendly greetings from people previously not known, new books and scientific papers, the bumbling of bees as they climb into the foxgloves, even the jumping of a frog seeming so strange and sudden gives a little thrill of conscious joy. These pleasures last and the mind seems more capable of understanding beauty than it used to be, but at the same time there grows up a form of sadness. It is a feeling of peculiar loss, or perhaps a realisation of all the ugliness the world contains, the cruelty of its people, the poverty, the stupidity and the lack of opportunity for many. This feeling of sadness and loss comes to nearly all who have lived for a while in an Arctic or Antarctic land. The feeling may be subdued by work and other concentrations, but at odd moments, suddenly and when alone, it leaps again into the consciousness. There grows a hunger that is not satisfied, a longing to go back to north or south, to live again to the full in a place unspoilt, to see men more nearly at their best, away from the greed and cruelty of warring nations, the lust for money and the lying tongues.

So visits anew are made, fleeting though they may be and in all too noisy aircraft. To the newcomer, travel in the tail-end is a progress within an elongate and chilly aluminium tube, six feet in diameter, cluttered with people, parachutes, emergency equipment and festoons of electrical and oxygen cables and connexions. Narrow slits enable sufficient views of the world around. Our course was due north up longitude 23° W. to the Pole. Leaving behind the rain and skerries of Iceland we saw the first pack-ice an hour and a half later and, soon after, Kapp Brewster, the southern headland of Scoresby Sund, the world's biggest fjord, on the east coast of Greenland. Then, in brilliant sunshine, we flew straight up Hurry Fjord and I could see with nostalgia and satisfaction the precise spot where I had spent a most happy summer nineteen years before. Then we sailed in our cockleshell among the floes, listened to the cries of the loons, and admired the bears and Musk Oxen: now we rushed through the air above, our metallic tube filled with the roar of engines, ourselves swollen with polar clothing and 'maewests'. Variety, as is well known, is the stimulant to the appreciation of life.

The east Greenland coast is an area of great beauty; an intricate fjord system; glistening ice as pack, berg and glacier; rocks pink, yellow and grey; sea blue and sparkling; distant ice sheet; crevasses green and tumbling icefalls. Meteorological good fortune shone brightly upon us and we were grateful. By a quarter to six in the afternoon, with the beauties of Peary Land on the port beam, a general haze developed and there was a mock sun travelling with us under the starboard wing. Greenland soon disappeared astern and we were over the Arctic Ocean with no land between us and the Pole, sky and cloud above, cloud and pack ice beneath.

Just before half-past six, after roughly nine hours in the air we reached 90° N. and turned to port heading for the Mackenzie delta. The navigators asserted that we had reached the North Pole. So far fortune had favoured us, but troubles soon began. A transfer cock from one fuel tank to the general system ceased to operate so that our effective fuel supply was, by that tank's capacity, diminished: we could not make Barter Island, the first emergency landing ground in our desired direction. So we turned for Thule, in north-west Greenland, and soon came in over the magnificence of northern Ellesmere Island and its great United States Range. Thule was not far off when my watch indicated 11 at night and I wrote in my notebook that the fjord complex contained no heavy ice. No further observation was set down until after the passage of some uncomfortable hours of stress, both physical and mental, for all of us. Mountains, clouds and ill-defined positions are an unfriendly trio for the pilot and the navigator. We finally landed four hours later, after a flight of nearly eighteen hours with no more than twenty minutes of available petrol in the tanks. The flight had all too admirably served its dual purpose as an exercise both in high latitude navigation and in flying towards the extremity of the fuel supply. Had we been living in earlier days we should on landing, like mariners saved from the sea, have at once set about building a chapel.

Great was our relief at last to land, neither on the sea nor on a nearby icecap, but with our wheels down on a runway; and to step out from the now sordid interior of the aircraft to a cool high Arctic dusk filled with hospitable Americans.

To me aerial travel is like dreaming: the scenes change all too swiftly; there is a lack of control and a lack of reality. Peculiar beauty abounds high above the earth, but it is a distant beauty, intangible, transitory and not fully satisfying. The contentment of spirit that can come from polar life and travel largely derives from the peace and silence of the icy land, the physical contact with the elements in all their moods, and the slow progress into the distance ahead. Friendship with one's dogs is real: I have never yet felt friendship for an engine.

Engines and contemplation can scarcely be compatible, unless perhaps for the congenital deaf, and the engine is today the epitome of civilisation, development, and exploitation, in the common usage of those words. The hermits of the past, lacking adequate clothes, have been near tropic dwellers but, adequately equipped, the polar regions can be paradise to the contemplative. Outside the expedition's little home the land is Nature's own; there are no man-made contrivances issuing forth smoke and filth, no noise of wheels and engines, no newspapers lying and spreading scandals, and no ugliness of any kind. The land is as God made it, filled with peace and beauty. Here a man may learn really to know his companions in a way impossible at home, where to know is so often merely to have an acquaintanceship, and what is more important, a man may learn to know himself, his failings and ignorance, no less than his ability and knowledge. Away from the constant distractions that make up the most of life at home, a man at last has the opportunity to think in peace. On sledging journeys, in the happy absence of machinery, when bad weather brings days on end of immobility in the tent, comes the time, so very rare in normal life, when a man, ill neither in mind nor body, can without any feeling of self-reproach or of work neglected, lie all day in pondering contemplation.* Besides the consideration of people, things and abstracts, there is time too for some analysis of the mind that thinks, a realisation of how it normally reacts, and how it might react if more carefully controlled. Days of lying-up in a tiny tent, even a week at a stretch is not a time of boredom, nor in modern days a period of discomfort, though certainly it is a time of deep regret that the work in hand cannot progress. But the weather is the working of a Providence that no man can control, and must therefore be accepted and forgotten. Then, the days of lying-up can become an increasing pleasure, filled with thought and daydreams, regrets, intentions, hopes and plans, realisations and resolutions in an ever-flowing stream. Yet it needs to be admitted that isolation and silence do not provide the way to contemplation and serenity for all men, and that even the polar regions now all too often blare with engines.

But even together, the physical and the mental, these do not make up the whole. Though the spiritual aspect is something more strictly personal, it would be wrong for that reason alone to set it aside from the present consideration. Some men are very conscious of this side of life, others are not, but there can be few who forget it completely, though they may profess to do so. On a polar expedition the beauty and the emptiness of the land, away from the works of men's hands, gives to many

* As well he can learn to play the mouth organ: hymn tunes are an easy start.

something of the feeling of the mystics and hermits, an escape from smallness and a readjustment of relative values. These feelings of human smallness and external greatness are intensified in times of trouble, and may leave a deep impression. Shackleton wrote (*South, The Sory of the* 1914-1917 *Expedition*): "When I look back at those days I have no doubt that Providence guided us, not only across those snow-fields, but across the storm-white seas that separated Elephant Island from our landing place on South Georgia. I know that during that long and racking march of thirty-six hours over the unnamed mountains and glaciers of South Georgia,* it seemed to me often that we were four, not three. I said nothing to my companions on the point, but afterwards, Worsley said to me, 'Boss, I had a curious feeling on the march that there was another person with us.' Crean confessed to the same idea. One feels 'the dearth of human words, the roughness of mortal speech' in trying to describe things intangible, but a record of our journeys would be incomplete without reference to a subject very near to our hearts." To most travellers in the empty places of the earth is given some measure of this feeling and for them the inscription over Scott's memorial, *Quaesivit Arcana Poli Videt Dei,*† takes on a deeper and a wider meaning.

* An important result of the work of the recent South Georgia survey, spread over several seasons, has been at last to delineate Shackleton's route. Indeed he was fortunate to succeed.

† Over the Scott Polar Research Institute, Cambridge:
"In seeking to unveil the Pole,
He found the hidden face of God."
—(Translated by The Reverend C. F. Angus.)

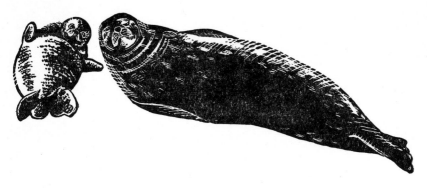